THE BOOK OF NASEEB

Khaled Nurul Hakim was born in Birmingham and has a background in film and poetry, publishing sparingly in the 1990s. He was visiting tutor in MA Screenwriting at the London College of Printing till 2004. *The Book of Naseeb* originally began as a 2005 screenplay for a low-budget feature film to be called *Barzakh*. Scheduled to be shot in Uzbekistan, the project was aborted when civil unrest broke out. Khaled took a decade-long break from writing to pursue a spiritual path, becoming a Sufi student and Sufi musician. He returned to rework the text as 'a degraded epic' while also looking after a growing family, a task that would take more than seven years.

ALSO BY KHALED NURUL HAKIM

POETRY

The Lost Poems (forthcoming, 2020)
Letters from the Takeaway (Shearsman, 2019)

The Book of Naseeb

KHALED NURUL HAKIM

Penned in the Margins

LONDON

PUBLISHED BY PENNED IN THE MARGINS
Toynbee Studios, 28 Commercial Street, London E1 6AB
www.pennedinthemargins.co.uk

First published in 2020

Printed in the United Kingdom by TJ International

ISBN
978-1-908058-74-4

CONTENTS

PART ONE | The Book of Naseeb   13

   The Mi'raj of Angels   15

   The Account of the Angel of the Right Hand   23

   The Account of the Angel of the Left Hand   49

   The Account of the Angel of the Right Hand   59

   The Night Journey   71

   The Night of Power   87

   The Night of Decrees   111

   The Account of the Angel of the Left Hand   151

PART TWO | Barzakh   157

GLOSSARY   321

ISLAMIC TERMS AND CONCEPTS

ANGELS

Jibreel
(also the *Ruh*) Archangel Gabriel, responsible for imparting messages from Allah;

Mikail
Archangel Michael, responsible for earthly phenomena and sustenance;

Israfil
Raphael, who blows the 'soor' or trumpet at end of the world;

Azrail
Angel of Death

Noble Scribes
(also called Receivers) *Arab. Kiraman Kaatibeen*, the recording angels of left and right who arrive at a person's age of responsibility, traditionally from eight years on

Protectors
(also called Followers) the protecting angels of front and back. Traditionally there is a changing of the watch at *Asr* (mid-afternoon) and *Fajr* (dawn)

Ruh
Arab. lit. 'Spirit', an epithet for Archangel Jibreel

Mi'raj	*Arab.* ascension (esp. Prophet's journey through the seven heavens)
Preserved Tablet	*Arab.* '*al Lawh al Mahfuz*', a metaphorical locus of the incorruptible Quran, created before time; it also holds the written destiny of every scintilla of the universe
Buraq	*Arab.* lit. 'lightning', fabled steed that transported the Prophet in his Night Journey
Ayah	*pl. ayat*, a Quranic verse; a sign, proof; a miracle. The Quran itself is counted as the greatest miracle, sign, and proof.
Barzakh	*Arab. Pers.* 'divide, barrier'. A place between Heaven and Earth where deceased souls await the final Judgement Day, where they may experience their own heaven or hell.

Salah	*Arab. pl. salat*, formal invocatory prayer at set times, *namaz* in Persian and Urdu
Magrib	*Arab.* lit. 'west', prayer at sunset. The Islamic day runs strictly from sunset to sunset
Esha	*Arab.* 'night', prayer at this time
Fajr	*Arab.* 'dawn', prayer at this time; time the angels change their watch (*Fajr khadib*: 'false dawn')
Zuhr	'midday', prayer at this time; on Friday this becomes congregational 'Jummah' prayer
Asr	*Arab.* 'mid-afternoon', prayer at this time; time the angels change their watch
Qiyam	*Arab.* lit. 'standing', a superogatory night prayer halfway between Esha and Fajr

Ramadan, Ramzaan *Arab.* ninth month in the Islamic calendar, month in which the Quran was first revealed, month of fasting

I'tikaf *Arab.* 'devoting', practice of spiritual retreat in mosque during last days of Ramadan

Laylatal Qadr *Arab.* variously translated as 'Night of Power', 'Night of Majesty', 'Night of Destiny or Decrees', 'Night of Measures'. In this night the year's decrees for all souls descends together with angels, departed souls, and gates of Hell.

Suhoor *Arab.* prescribed meal before dawn during Ramadan

Taraweeh *Arab.* lit. 'refreshment', superogatory Ramadan night prayers after Esha, reciting a *juz* (group of Quran chapters)

A full glossary appears on page 319.

Asterisked speech in italics denotes that it is dialect; unasterisked speech in the same dialogue denotes reversion to English.

to the Author of all

Part One

The Book
of Naseeb

1 | *The Mi'raj of Angels*

In which the Archangel Jibreel gathers the Recording Angels and Protecting Angels and instructs them of their charge; and they mark the fate of the soul in the Preserved Tablet; and make the *mi'raj* to his world.

§

Read! In the name of your Lord, who created, created from a clot, and assigned each soul Receivers, to record in truth; and from these no thought is hidden, no scornful word unheard, and from whose Pens naught shall go unwrit.

And at the fiat of Jibreel, we gathered in the lowest sphere within the compass of a grain. And a thousand angels brought down the Preserved Tablet wherein all is decreed.

Read! said the Ruh, and stretched thousandfold Wings bounding the geometry of our world around a drop of sea.

And I saw archangel Israfil flicker into a trumpet-blowing messenger in gorgeous flowing green and turban, and his lips poised to blow for Judgement Day. And heavyclouded Mikael with his angel hosts who would drive the wind and rain and sea before them.

Read! That your Lord who knows the fall of a sparrow's egg is content to hear the Accounts from the Recorders of the Right and Left Hand; and these, from the tangle of human motives, assign each deed to good and bad. And given to you, Roquib, precedence over Atid of the Left Hand, that you may allot tenfold or seven hundredfold merits to a completed good deed. And Allah is Merciful, All-Knowing.

How many Angels assemble at the blast? Protectors and Scribes for every soul ever born.

Some mystics imagine our world so well that in their minds it assumes a shape. But this shape has no top or bottom, it is not coloured, it has no weight. Truly our substance is infinitely stiff, infinitely pliant. We vibrate as one with no delay and no wave motion. Nevertheless the blast of Israfil's horn disturbs a boat on a calm lake.

And given each soul two Followers, front and rear, to ward off evil. And these are with him from the womb—And the Protectors Hamza and Alif, the Protectors emerge from the waves.

An Angel is a fine and wonderful thing, almost amphibian between being and not being; as elastic deformation, or variation of pressure or electrical or magnetic intensity, or temperature. The water does not move forward, only the shape of the wave. And the boat oscillates up and down.

And we gazed on the Preserved Tablet.

There in a lambent lake of calligraphy the last of his words shine in the skinless surface—the filamental floaters of a life trembling, trembling in the Eye of the Creator.

Ah, what can describe the Preserved Tablet wherein the Book is writ?

Some see a hundred stark woods against a grey sky, each instant shuttling aspen, ash, and elms; with only a rumble of autumn wind against the flash of branches. Some see ten thousand bells of jellyfish, pulsing with luciferin blue and pink, and look through streams of tendrils, and plankton and arthropods twitching in the solid sea.

These unformed signs, the unformed signs before *alif* was formed.

The Archangel dips a Wing in the skinless surface of the Book.

And we descry the creature's face in the lake. There in his eyes it is we who are holding him down, our shadows wobbling in skeins of light, as he drowns in a scumstained bath. The water yammering in his ears. Then our shapes explode in shards. And his life flashes before him...

And we thought: *If he is dying, who is this old man and boy? Rifle and ammunition slung from shoulder and hips, scraping*

down the mountain track, a box wrapped in jute strapped to the back
of the old farmer. And a scrawny pale horse or donkey weighed down
with a crate. Lines drawn in dust in the old man's face, who is not as
old as he looks, and the strippling the same...

... the boy against the pack animal, salwar kameezes flapping
as knees buckle on the ruts. The man's eyes fixed on the path, passing
words with his son as they clamber down. The track flushing down
into a white road bounded by ridges.

(And each Night of Decree, when the year is revealed for
the soul, we watch this vision of his end.)

We dive into the Book of Naseeb.

We dive into a lake of kelp. As far as we look the canopy
sways with the surge, full of gaps and full of lights. Pregnant with
all past and future. Blue rockfish and kelp blades flash blank
surfaces. Bristleworm, scud and eelgrass deform into signs...

Read!

... When their mother came in, Arif gets up and turns to the
wall.

... A dog smeared in excrement and blood runs down the
street on three legs, looking back at him, beseeching.

... The creature goes to stay with his mother after youth
detention. Every memory of her, she's looking over her shoulder while

he hurries after.

… They wheel around and smash an umbrella in his face. He runs home crying and cupping the blood in his hands. His father took him to the hospital and says, You want injection? The nurse has to stitch up the boy's face without anaesthetic.

… The boy sprang up and into the sack and bounded from the others; but the headmaster stopped the race, for his sack has a hole.

His life flits by as sea cucumber and bat star…

And here, his first page!—*a boy of ten in oversized Rambo T-shirt playing with other hazel-eyed children outside the white-walled house. On the flat roof the big girls play badminton, bunches of iron supports sprouting around them. And he's trying to get the kids in kurtas to play dusty football between gates that drape buntings and banners as if expecting the next wedding party.*

Abba and Chacha, moustached and paunched in their kurtas, and his brother Arif get into the minivan with darkened windows.

He runs crying Baba! Chacha!, hanging on the door handle as it edges out. His father barking rebuke; Chacha, ever indulgent, lets him in.

And in the minivan they feed him pistachios, Arif glowering on the back seat even then—(how he misses his bullying!).

—*Eat, boy. Why don't you eat? Bhaiya, why is he so thin? It's not right for a Londoni.

—*I beat them—do they eat? It's their mother's fault.

(Where is his mother? She should be there, a soft buffer smelling of eau de toilette and sunscreen in her white headscarf and scorched skin. If she was there, snug between...)

Cigarette smoke gusting round and out the windows; he and Arif slyly kick each other.

Driving across arid plains. Everything the colour of lime. Then the fields of poppy. Mujahadeen stand in the orange heads, nicking poppy bulbs with a knife and screwing up their faces. (Somewhere the farmer and son stumble down the mountain track with the skinny pale horse or donkey.)

There in the border bazaar—tape recorders blaring distorted Quran, greasy Kalashnikovs, ammunition rounds, mortars on the stalls. Abba and Chacha cross-legged with jummah-going shop owners on the wooden stoops. And a bearded mullah leans forward, sober waistcoat criss-crossed with ammunition belts, to pinch his cheek (Naseeb, nai?), and a swell of pride tingles his ears.

They talk more and Chacha takes out a bundle of notes and puts it on the stoop.

And then he and Arif hold a Kalashnikov, and Abba fires in the air.

And now here, sneaking a glimpse in the backyard with Arif—the menfolk at some alchemy with a narrow trough of treacle giving off fumes, the blazing firewood in the afternoon not warmer than the grateful lump of love he feels, this privileged men's world of Abba and Chacha and Arif...

Is this how he will remember dying?

Where, then, is Azrael, Archangel of Death? In the towering trunks of kelp stipes, the shadow of a grey whale so enormous it goes unseen.

And we hear the blast of Israfil's horn smashing through the waters, and we arrow back to the surface.

And at the fiat of the *Ruh* Jibreel, we gathered in the lowest sphere within the compass of a grain.

And received the Book and the boy.

Henceforth are you confined to the slave, paired to record the Truth, which lies in the other's hidden region. And created in symmetries, that you may succeed each other in the watches of the day, and the watches of the night. And your zaat as Angel-shaped threads from this world to the world of creatures. And your Lord is Merciful, Kind.

And Mikael of the wind and rain and sea and earth, and his angel hosts, made ready to translate to the realm of creatures. And he stretched thousandfold Wings.

Ten billion Angels feel the fluctuations. And at this instant we become Followers and Scribes for every soul ever born.

And with them the Noble Atid and I made ready to translate to the place of the creature. And the Relieving Angels keep a heartshaped lake till the appointed time.

Khoda hafiz, we say to each other, *What you observe, we observe. As you are there, we are there.*

An exploding horizon of Wings.

We cascade down shearing radiance, our faces burnt from the limitless sun, to receive a boy of ten in Rambo T-shirt, with the hazel-eyed children outside the white-walled house, and together dance with him, together dance with him to death.

2 | *The Account of the Angel of the Right Hand*

In which Your creature seeks his misfortune with the help of Angels and men; and is confounded by a drop of Mercy from a woman; and dreams of doing good; and finds his misfortune removed.

§

(Asr: 1605 GMT)

Da man runs out of his flat wiv da left luggige ticket.

An his Protectors front and back. Arownd dere transparence dey assume da semblans of cortiers from Samarkand. And dese have folowed him from da womb.

And I say to them:

Assalaamu alaykum Hamza, assalaamu alaykum Alif, how gos da servant?

Greetings, O Noble Scribes, you tell us, sez Hamza. *We just wipe his bum.*

Yr servant runs out of da flat wiv da left luggige ticket. Its mundane paper shining wiv *baraka*, to be exchangd for a black polythen parcel; dats gonna tumble out his Golden Fleece, gilding his face wif bliss, O shining faces of da blessed! *I pray You Lord,* his hert beats, *Save this sad creture, for I am f___d. May I be truly thankful. Amen.*

Da creature floors da clapping motor. Da whole way vex by da yowling yute, da yowling babby in th back o da car, and a fear th ticket wud fly out of his pocket.

—Todays da day, bway! Redistrbute som welth. Make em pay! Trust me. Yu gonna ride shotgun for me? You da Man! I need yu.

But da babby is bawling snot in his babychair.

—Hey, Jonah! Lern som history, mistah. You payin attenshion? We won da war for dem goore. *Us Pathans, bwoy. Understand? Hanh. So now we're helping arselves.* Ey, bill up for me, geeza... for fffaaa... Hey, Jonah...!

But da babby is bawling snot.

And under his breth, *Shut da fff-flip up, man.*

(Careful of his hart, Naseeb. Th child doz not know riht and rong. His Protecting Angels strong.)

—Yu shud a met my Legal. He'da educated ya. Wots one crime when yu got British come n screw evryone over? But you knock over one old boy, an da hole machinery comes down on ya!

But da pickney yowls for his bottel.

I rite his words, *I get you da juce, I get you da juce,* as one good deed. And my noble Atid will sternly smile an say, *Let him turn the car rownd. I'll giv him a thozand merits.*

And da car swerving as da servant gropes for a baby botle.

—Here, cane it. Only Jonah, yu gotta fix up, look da part, get me? I cant do this without yu. Blatant. Yore my sideman. Anyone com near me, yore da mouth.

And da Protectors wrap dere powers around da car to stop it swerving. And perhaps, perhaps dere was an atoms waiht of kindnes for da child. And praps I shud record it as ten good deeds.

Da road to Heethrow is alwayz rosting.

Yor creture floors da clapping motor.

Aw, we are breezin, cry Hamza an Alif, striking fihting pozes on da hood n roof, thoh assuming da semblans of cortiers from Samarkand—thir green tunic and turban tails ripping: *Wet dat motor, bossman!* And da child's Protectors cry, *Maashallah*, and a liht blazed whirling from his weels.

And if you cud see a Caravan of Protectors poized on bonnets an hoods in da jam from Northolt!—thir wite robes or black tunics ripping, or as elastic deformasion, or electrical or magnetic intensity…

And in de airport da cretur clings like begfrend to da child. In his hand da left luggig tiket. Its mundane paper shining wif *baraka*.

An he mutters to himself not to talk, he mutters himself not to talk. Da luggige atendant finks hes got a mental condicion. Da ticket soked wiv swet.

And despar filld his univers as de atendant disapeared in da back. Da Feds about to absail out da sky and bang him up in a meat wagon.

Da pickney griping.

And do you see da African cleener dragging her polythen bag? Yea, shes bin lost here forever. Dere's djinn in every airport!

Dat djinn, shes gonna mess wiv his head, sez Alif.

And her litter picker clips da cretures foot till hes vex.

Sorry, my dear, shes mumbling.

An his patting da child bare vexed. An he finks he hears her mumble, *Are you all waiting with dis gentleman?*

The atendant com back wiv a babby's green holdall. And Noble Atid waches da slaves neck. Surely dey see his neck vein pulse! And Noble Atid wispers: *Dey know, dey know wat yu do. Yore blatant.*

But Naseeb lifts the exquizit heft.

And da pickney Jonah griping.

Da Followers throw dere sheeld arond. But dat creaturs

lost his hart, his feet cant goo strait. And he sits with Jonah, whoz soaked in s__t. An he cant think straiht. And he feels in da green bag. Feels for a nappy. Feels for a polathene bag packt in Peshawar.

And his Protectors assume da semblans of two airport Feds. To mess wiv his hed. Two airport Feds com from the other side o th concorse. And Yor slave hears handsets jammed wiv noiz, feels them standing dere wif agate eyes.

An his hand grips da polathene in da bag.

And the babby stares at dem. Soaked in s__t.

And Five-O smiling back. Da pickney's Protectors, immezurably strong, say: *Pooh! I think the babys trying to tell you somthing.*

An next man Hamza raizes his MP5 and farts: *Well put that on th record!*

Astaughfirullah, and Noble Atid rasps on dere walkie-talkie: *Back to yr stacions, gentelmen.*

And dey melt back.

Dat creturs rooted. Till Jonah starts howling. And he legs it to the exit—da pickney howling, Five-O about to absail out da sky, his body so hype it wud a shattered if somone askt direcsions.

And Noble Atid wispering: *They know wat you do, they kno wat you do.*

Da carpark streches as far as da rack and wind of Mikail

spanning horizons with his wings. And still no one stops da slave.

When he reches da car Yor servant triz to clean da scribeless child. Yea, an innocent stepdad wiv his Pampers. But hes shat up to his neck. Screaming Old Bill down. An da servant trying to wipe him wid da babygrow and hose him with a bottle a water.

Jesus, he weeps, *Plese, Jesus.*

Yea Yor creture stuffs da soiled garms in a carryer bag. And unzips da baby holdall. (Packt in Peshawar two weeks ago. Da Companion of da Left Hand recorded it). Now he tekes out a blak polathene parcel and sticks it in da cronic nappy bag n ties it up.

Da future like a garden o grassy eaze & largess, an companionable houris wif sherbet—he can tuch it!

Da slave drives dazed. Somewere up da motorway he miht crash, an da pickney inherit a kilo of smack.

Da Followers throw dere shield around da car. As if they cud deflect his corse an atom's bredth.

As if they cud protect him when da car lost power. When da car lost power arond da island he almost passes out.

Da Protectors for da child, immezurably strong, asume da semblans of da Sahaba: *O Followers! Man yor frail bark! Catch the dowtful wind and eaze him to his reward.*

Da Followers for Naseeb cry battle criez, flash agate eyes,

Ya Seen! Haul to, Protectors! Keep this bag o nails straiht, Alif! Ya Seen! Ya Seen!

The Protectors for da scrybeless child, thir wite robes ripping, flash dark: *Yallah, habibin, lets speed him to his doom! Allahu Akbar!*

Dey chant da battle criz o da Sahaba, *Ta Ha! Ta Ha!* And thir Powers crackle.

Da pickney Jonah slept.

Dat creatur drove round twice arond da block befor he parks.

And walking up da starewell, babby in one arm, two bags in the other, Yur slave he trembles.

Yea, deres more dred letters on da mat. And Alif shoots out a protectif shield: *Long as he doznt open them his safe.*

An he checks Alesha's shift.

Put da pickney in bed.

Put a green bag on da kichen table.

Owner of da World.

(Maghrib: 1759 GMT)

Da slave cuts da smack.

But da Noble Scribe must stay his entry, for dis creatur may yet repent or pray.

Blazing a spliff as he weiys again. Digital scales. Starch. Polathene bags. Razor blade.

And da scribeless babby waching in th doorway, gets pushd away to a video. But da babby wants to wach.

Thru his eyes.

Dat slave hes teazing into score bags.

—End of th day ya cyaant beat da painkillin propertys of ma erb, mon. What you say? Hanh? They make a natural plant ilegal innit... They want ya to buy billions of asprins an s__t. But yu get natural herb yeh—like s__tlodes a medical benefits—

And one of his fones is warbling.

—Jonah, get that for us.

An he chups his teeth an skins up and checks da caller. Coz he never ansers.

And da babby maks a dash for da bags. And Yor creture scolds him in Pashtu:

—*Ey ey ey—not till you do som work arond th house!*

And Jonah yowling. Dat slave he hurriz to seal da bags. And hes cooing baby Urdu wif a blade a powder:

—*Nice—tasty tasty... Baby num num. Why dont you eat? Peple died so you coud have a taste.*

An da slave makes th call to Ali.

—Nice num num... Ali Baba! Salaamalaykum! Heh heh

heh. Good, *chacha*. Got something for ya... Yeh man, yeh man— Im a big boy now. Ain it... I cant, boss. I cant just yet. Paciense, *chacha*. So how soon we sort this? Oh, com man—deyr gonna loze this! I need it upfront—dis aint smalltime s__t... *Pacience, chacha, paciense. I'll let you kno.* Yeah, you let me know, I got peple on hold... I gotta sort few ting. Few ting ain it... Heheheh, yehman. You an me *chacha*! I tole you wed make a team!

Truly, blazing his weed not warmer dan this love he feels, of Chacha an him.

Dat creatur clears da kichen.

Doz he not see? Jonah bilding his own works—toy cash register, Play-Doh, packets a Hula Hoops, plastic nife: cutting a pece of playdo an puting it into a packet, shuffling Hula Hoops into another, wayhing it on da scale...

The agate eyes of da Noble Scrybe they see.

Dere was a text in dred capitals:

BAILIFFS due to remove your GOODS. Call NEWKEY on 01604 100341 to stop this. Quote ref 1928150. Do not text.

Just da capitals got his body flooding angwish agen.

But what dett is this? Hes almost pissed enuf to call them.

And he goos in the bedroom to pick out a prosthetic shell. One of his collecsion of prosthetic legs for his plans to help da limmless. To help da limmless in Peshawar n Kabul.

And he packs da score bags in a leg.

Dat creture hears her key—Aleshas key in th door—and jumps to stick a spoon a mush in da child. And her Protector's Wings dey riffle in da hall. Her Protectors wrap dere wings round Leesha's bump as she bends down to pick up letters.

And Alif and Hamza shear across her Followers, an put dere faces in Leesha's bump. And say to da Angel of da Womb, *Ya Rabbi, a drop of seed? Ya Rabbi, a clot? Ya Rabbi, a morsel of flesh?* And as far as dey look da canopy sways, and protectors twitching in da solid sea. Dat pulses now wif *baraka*.

And our creture doznt know about her woom.

She smells him pengin up da flat, and throws down unregenerat letters, and looks at da mess.

And Yor creture:

—I tryd to get him to vacuum but he wudnt have it.

—For Godsake, Naseeb. You havnt changd him.

Dat servant drops th demands on th table. (His debt collecsions gather in a shoebox. Dose at da bottom she must never see).

And as she screws, de Followers mimic to de babby: *We shud talk, this isnt going anywere, hav yu got a job, blah blah...*

Yor creatur teks a zoot from his ear:

—*Eat, eat, boy. Take a long drag. Why dont you eat?*

Say, wat does Jonah want in da kichen?

—Thats alriht, Jonah. You'll haf to make do with me. Uncle Naseeb has got more important things. Never mind yore going to get nappy rash. What do you want, Jonah? You cant have that! Yes yes, Im th horrible one. I keep th flat going. I keep th car on th rode. I arrange the daycare while he flys off somwere. Probbly to visit his child bride.

And as shes screwing at him Yor creature mimics to da babby:

—We shud talk, this isnt going anywhere, have you got a job, blah blah...

And she swept up her child to change him, change him in da bedroom.

—She can com over here if she likes. Do som laundry. Id like a holiday... Wud you lik to stay with him wile I vizit his other wives? You cudnt call him Dad thoh. Coz he doznt relly want to be with us. Some men, they just need a base. Somone stupid they can tap when they like.

—Yes dear. Thats riht.

She kisses her babby fiercly as he whinges.

—Im sorry, Jonah. You dezerve better. An yuve seen too much. Mummy gets too... She doznt give you enuf priority.

And sweeping in an out of rooms to hang out cloze and

put another load in. And da scribeless child gone back to his dealers game: cutting his stash o Mini Cheddars wiv Playdo an weyhing da packets on his scale.

(And Noble Atid: *By no means can he be distracted!*)

And Yor creture feels her:

Wots da beeyatch screwing at now?

And da slave finds her wif da green baby bag.

—I bowht it for Jonah.

Ah, she feels him—taking it from her hands and into da bedroom. Were he scwirrels it behind da wardrob.

Ah, she feels him. Do ye see her scoping da kichen? And th scales. Yea, and in da swing bin: a ball o black plastic taped tihte. A razor blade.

Dat servant feels her stomak fall sume place. (Da Followers for da Mother fan balm into her nose.) Ach! She hears dat slave cum back. But she didnt speak. For if she asked him he wud lie. (Wud he not lie?) And it wud come out in da spitting confrontasion. And cud she throw him out agen?

And da Mother went in da bedroom. And Yor creture felt her. An da child came into th living room wiv his scales.

And he herd her: *I dont want this!*

Dat mutha come in with artificial limms in ech hand, in

ech hand a limb dat she threw at him!

Yor creturs hart contracts. And Alif & Hamza block wiv *silat* moves—as if they cud deflect an atom!

—I dont want this s__t arond Jonah!

Dat slave cud smack her up da head.

The Scribes of da Left Hands note thir words as they screw at ech other.

Do you see Naseeb baling on her now? And smuggling out his collecsion o limbs? Smuggling his legs & hands into her carboot, to salvige som tokens of his dreme. Look at him chasing his dreme... Can I rite som attribute of goodnes clings to these gifts to da poor an orphaned? And dat, somewere, his intenshion is pure?

(Esha: 1945 GMT)

Da creture thowt about driving Leeshas whip to Fat Tone's, but hes bare shook about da kilo in Leeshas boot. And he calls his spar Zak, he called his spar to pick him up.

And he brings out da last leg to jam into her boot.

By the silver Audi dat parks at Leeshas. And da sodium street lite. And dat servant Zak, his Angels hugging da shaved lines in his hed.

And sez Naseeb:

—I need you with me, geez.

—Deres baggamans screwin you done a runner Naz.

—Wot you chattin? Dat s__t is all rinsed. What they sayin?

—Gonna murkalise you bruv.

Yor creture stares a bit. (*Jam, brah, we got your back*, sez Hamza). Then he fishes in da boot and beckons da servant Zak.

—Yeah? You wanna see my protector? Deyr gonna think twice befor they mess wiv dis s__t.

—Yor what?

Yor creture scoping arond.

—Dis ting is mint! Old scool, bway, old scool.

—Nah man.

—Com man, feel it. Ting is antiq.

—Thats bait blud. You cant be flashing dat araond.

—Wot you on about? I aint gonna use it. Ting is just for ni-iceness.

And Naseeb threw his ting from da boot and da Followers for Zak throw a sheeld around him, an dat cretur halfspins around. An a prosthetic hand hit him over his Calvins and smacks to da ground.

—Rah!

And his dumb spar kicks away da hand, and Yor creture

goz:

—Oi! Go eazy with ma gat!

And Yor creture examins da hand for scratches & Zach looks in da boot at da rest o th haul.

—Dat is som sick mash cuz.

For bridges got burnt running to Pakistan. And word went out and dere were twelve yer old wannabees redy to jack Yor creatur. He needs to speak to one of da faces. Coz its a mistake. He never ripped em off. He'll pay it back.

And Yor slave didnt wanna leve his legs, he didn wanna go Zaks ride and leve a kilo in her boot.

Jam, brah, we got yor back, sez Alif.

And dey extend thir Wings round Leeshas car.

And Noble Atid sez, *As tho ye change whats coming by a hairs bredth.*

And Hamza sez, *Why, wots coming?*

And if you cud see Protecters poized on bonnets n hoods speeding to Stonbrigge Park!—thir wite robes or black tunics ripping, or as elastic deformasion, or electrical or magnetic intensity…

And dat slave was finking bout his dreme in Leeshas boot da hole ride.

(Taraweeh: 2105 GMT)

And outside Fat Tones street his bruckup Escort was on da street.

Dey sat in the Escort getting licky on Fat Tones draw.

An da Protecting Angels dissipate in da penging air. Sumewere on da hood deys busting *silat* moves n chattin air still. And thir Powers etiolated as gnat water.

And Yor creture sez:

—I need a coupla hundred, boss.

Da radio on, drum shakes da plastic dashbord. Fat Tone blazing a spliff. He aint saying nuffin.

Yore creture sez:

—Five years, Tone.

—Wot?

—Retire, innit. I cud a bin out alredy. I tell you bout my legal rep? He had his own supplier, but if I couda got in that... Professhnals, you imagin?

—Bun dat, boys.

—Its trade innit. Blatant. Only way anyone invest in the Fird World. Doze lawyers an media gash Id see—deyre keeping Bolivian pezants alive! I tole you, we shud go Class A. Time the Afghani farmers got in da game. Wot you think? Put your boyz to work.

—Im makin a move myself bruv.

—Giving you a chance to bring in da big dollars innit.

—Nah man. I need ma papers.

Busting ninety quid crepes up on da dash.

—You gonna lose dis geezer. I'll front you da bags.

—Nah man.

—You dont wanna be baddest brer on road?

The air thick wiv fug and edge.

—Im already big in th game.

Yor creature sees, dat bony goofus poized to mark his yard.

—Yeah? Wha is th game?

Dat bony slave not bothered by a deddout older:

—Geezer, I am the game.

And th creture Zak is tracing shaved lines in his hed.

—Yeah? Its all jokes tho, innit? You got som face making da papers, driving flash car, propa don n that. An he cant even leve his yard. Living wiv his mom an everythin. Wats that about?

And Fat Tone seething:

—Its all bless.

Dat slave left them to his bruckup wheels and sloped away.

Somwere on da roof da Followers mimic da singer

quacking about da papers hes stackin, da blocks on hold, his workers n shootas... Somwere on da roof dere busting silat moves, thir Powers as weak as water.

—Yu know how much wele make off a kilo of brown? Kilo and a half. Cane it...

And his spar, whoz almost invizible, took da spliff. And didnt say nuffin.

—Cant be a wasteman all yr life. You wanna be shotting weed for him all day?

—I aint dat any more.

—Wot, you above all that? Dont tell me you still playing yor gay choons with thoz jokers?

—I dunno. Its gonna affect things tho innit.

—Wot you on about? Hows it affect thos Afganis? Theyr looking after themselvz, ennit? You gorra look after yrself in this life...Yeah, but Im puttin back. Check me, Im opening up a hospital on th border. Yu know that? Yeh-man, help da cripples wiv thir legs an s__t. Dats wot this is about. So wot you think?

And his spar is saying nuffink.

And dey silent listening to drum. And Yr slave getting vex wiv Fat Tone and Zak and grimey singers on da radio.

—Who is dis whiney batty don?

—I dunno.

—Dook that little s__t up. I dunno what da yute listning to these days.

And his buzz gone sour.

—You wanna go home?

Dat servant drops Naseeb off back to his yard.

And da Noble Followers emerge from dissipacion. Dey rap thin chill around Yor slave.

And thoh his buzz was sour, and da Followers emerge from dissipacion, Yor creature was too mash to check Aleeshas car. And da Protectors throw a vail over his eyes: were under the jaundisd street lite Aleeshas car had an orange clamp chained to da front weel.

Truly, his hert wud freeze an the ignominy of da weak wud overwelm! And a hundred bills swirl in his belly.

But da Followers throw a vail over his eyes and he didn see were da council had clampt da front weel.

And in da stairwell he called Ali.

—Salaam, Chaccha! Whassa news, boss?... I thowt you told him that!... I thot you told him that! Get him down man. This geezers worrying me. I cuda found somone myself... How longs he need? Dats bollocks! Im takin it easy! I got peple lined up this end, Im takin it eazy. Tell him he aint getting nu'in til I see it upfront... He knos we need it upfront. Whatdaaa...

Dat slave cusses and kicks da wall. Wile his uncle jams his hype. Yea, wile his uncle has his back.

—Iss bollocks... Im calm tho, innit. Yeeah, pashiens. Dumbshit. Listen, you keep on him, Chacha. Salaam. All rite. Laters.

This grateful lump of love.

Da Protectors wrap thir Powers around.

He saw two spots of color in her cheek he knew wud be ther for days. He needs to find another hiding place.

And she spoke about thir finances. He sez hes wiped out after Pakistan.

Say, she wanna smack his head up *tchaa*, leve scratches on his neck, teeth in his cheek. But she need to take care, she need ta breathe. (He doznt know she need to take care, she need ta breathe. An his sins are not multiplied)

—You remember th woman at Citizens Advice? She sed you have to rite to th banks.

Becoz you told th dole we were shacked up, he thot, *and dey closed all my claims; and taxing me six months. A Pataan, wiv da blood of mountain clans, reared to raid da lowlands, jack the women, fight da kuffar, begging th Housing Benefit.*

—Im waitin to hear back, he sez.

Yor creture sees da razor blade in da kichen.

He wants to sleep but needed her to go to bed. To go and get his bag o dreams from her car and find another hiding place.

Say, she cud smell it off him. And she was gon to bed.

Yor creetur plugged in Doom 3. And qwikly desends to th dead.

And Hamza sez: *Noble Alif, we's gonna be mongin out tonite.*

And da Followers wandering corridors of the damned with vacant bludlust.

Ech time Yor creature makes a gesture his road forks off; we follow passages branching infinitly, and we will never find our way back.

(Qiyam: 0045 GMT)

At som point Yr creture realized she is standing in the doorway.

Dat servant waits for him to die.

And her Followers fan balm in her face.

He wanted to looze himself in da sepulkers of his game. But shes standing ther.

—I hope theyre helping you to find somthing. I know what its like to be skint... And yu can stay away from... the others yu were... coz I cant afford to have it in the flat.

Her eyes water; thow his hackles ar up he is disarmed.

—We cant looz this flat, Nassa... you kno that.

—Safe.

Hav you seen a woman with mercy? Her tears coming and her voyse wobble? Her Folowers, they blow into her face.

—It makes me get crazy wen were like this. I just dont know wat yore doing. You dont tell me, Nassa. You can help me by telling me. If yore not motivated or... it must be hard to start all over and not find... I do appreshiate... Id rather you took a paper round than went bak to all that... I dont mind being the bredwinner.

Tho his hackles are up he is cawt.

—Im sorry I get crazy somtimes. I just dont want to get to th point its just wharever. I dont want us to pretend. You can tell me, Nassa.

Truly, thez cretures hear the Angels listening.

And he flinchd.

—Som day we mite have a kid. It wud be nice for... an make a home. If yuve thot of... We just need to communicate. You can tell me.

—Safe.

—Id like you to tell me. Wat yu want to say. If yu want

to think about it. You can tell me wen you want to say... Did you want to say anything?

Alhamdulillah.

And he is full of wonder. Why did she do that just now? Who was she?

Yor servant stays up wondering how he got here. Today he saw a frog cringing under somwuns wall.

And he cant find wich Naseeb to remember. A yearning spot dat wants to dash th Plan. To sacrifice da Game and go strait to th sunny garden of cripples n pleazantries and fruits of doing Good.

(*An he became a saint*, sez my Noble Scribe.)

He needed her to sleep. To get da green baby bag from da bedroom n go to her car.

Da creature crept into da room. Wid da Protectors becalming her sleep. But da bag it hisst between da wardrobe and da wall ware he stashed it. And her voyce come slow:

—And remember she sed you can rite to th credit cards.

—I alredy did.

—Do you need th car tomorrow? I need it later.

—Yeah, he sez.

Say, he cant remember why he hadnt written da letters to th banks an cards. But dere was so much to do, so many things.

Who cud do it all? Dey want him to swet all dis pointless stuff. Dey have no idea. He has to do wat his destiny sed. His vizion becom known, his risktaking vindicated. And peple retributed.

And da slave wanted to loze himself in da sepulkers of th game.

He didn know when he slept.

The soul dreamed of taking fifteen hundred arms and legs to Afghanistan.

He was in a factory plant with prosthetic shells sprayed by robots.

Down featureless corridors of a storage centre, the rows of corrugate metal rooms under striplights swaying on wire, where a sad orphan that never found its stump was caged.

The din of metal beaters and furnace, and the corrugate walls and chickenwire ceilings open onto a workshop garage in India. Children in vests and halfshirts gawk at a young man getting his foot keel fitted. And the khaki'd police lounge at the shutters.

And then they play football in the street, the amputee in three-quarter combats bounding along, another small boy with Himalayan eyes galloping on titanium pylon and wooden feet, the children surging fish shoal...

When Yor servant wakes it takes a bit before he realized it waznt real and hes got nothing heroik to tell.

And he rolls out of da sofa to his fones flashing in da unlit living room wiv missed calls from unnown numbers.

And drawn to da spare room, to stand in front of da winda and look at Leeshas car and sense da goods still there, a ghost cum back to unfinished matter. He cud tuch it—da future like a garden o grassy eaze an largess, and companionable hooris with sweet drinks—so hard not to hold it!

And da Protecters removed da vail from his eyes, whare under th jaundisd street lite Aleeshas car was gon.

And still he didnt see it.

He wants to go to bed. But his wondering were he parked da car. And sumfing starts lurching thru him. Till hes awake.

And he dozent see the car. But he sees da keys on th table.

And he wen out to the car. Where under the jaundisd lite Aleeshas whip is gone.

And he wandered th streets, coming back to ech one as tho hes made a mistake. As tho dere was a secret slip road in his hed.

But dis was da spot.

An time and space shud be here. (But da Counsil hirelings in thir lorry had come).

Ther is da slave calling on his fones. But no one is awake. And he has to go back to th flat.

By th leaking liht draping th duvet as it rose and fell wid her breething...

Why did she cume to him like that? Like he cud tell her everything.

And abased, da belever calls out, *Wake up, Leesha. Wake up. Drag it all out of me. Let me fall on th hollows of yr hips and call out Save me. Save me, Leesha. Say you forgive me. Coz I cant drag my life back.*

(Fajr: 0547 GMT)

Say! My Companions sens the enormus wings, da pressure drop of electric storm. Noble Atid looks at me to say, *The time is here, our watch is over, till* Asr *come agen.*

And his account may now be fixt, and deeds alloted to good n bad.

And Angels of sucsesion are passing along a thred to this relm. But we are alredy asending da Empyreans, pinned back by da wait of hopeless Mercy, and I hav alredy forgotten. Each time we return, it is as thoh we were never here. And we too shall be askd by the Uneeq One, *How did you find My servant? And how did you leve My servant?*

3 | The Account of the Angel of the Left Hand

In which the Recording Angels return on the fabled Buraq to the Archangel Jibreel; and present the creature's record; and find the Account of the Left Hand is written; and read his struggle to regain his misfortune; and make the mi'raj back to his world.

§

We are carried on the firebird wings of the Buraq. And looking on his grave moonface, his arching Persian brows, with bearing of earnest young mufti, and head perched on dapplegold neck of a horse, I wonder that he has no arms to eat with. Somewhere the Buraq was described as a spotless steed with noble head, and so they pictured a human face. And our Powers pictured as parrot wings.

But then what shape is ours? We have not top nor bottom, nor colour, nor weight. Truly our substance is infinitely stiff, infinitely pliant.

What if you could eat grass or oats, says Hamza.

We do not eat gross material, says the Buraq.

But what if, say, I feed you bran mash? How could you eat enough to nourish a horse's frame?

We nourish ourselves by His radiance, by worship.

Yes, but what if, says Alif.

Sometimes they chafe him that his wings should sprout from his shoulders or feet, as Persian pictures. The Buraq will ever play perplexed. They have been playing this game for ten thousand years. That is the gift of *Jannah*—that he fails not to be perplexed, and we fail not to be pleased.

We carry on his wings to the lowest Heaven. And come to an endless plain of serried Angels that ripple to the horizon in *salat*. And as they flow in waves of standing bowing prostrating, they articulate the fleeting *ayat* of the Book.

And at the fiat of Jibreel, the plain is bent until its ends encompass a grain, and Protectors and Scribes for every soul are gathered in a drop of sea.

And the *Ruh* dips a Wing in the skinless surface. And in it we look on our own creatures.

And we descry the shadows of our wretch's end wobbling in a solid sea, our shadows holding him in a scumstained bath, and a fist that bursts the surface, and our shapes that burst into shards.

And how did ye leave your creatures, says the Ruh.

And the wretch's page unfolds as a wrinkled grey sea. And now my Noble Roquib's *shikeste* hand flashes on the creeping waves. These ayat of dancing lines slanting from imagined corners, and arching up and down like blossom spray. And margins sprouting commentary and calligram.

And my Noble Roquib says: *The servant is praying.*

(The creature is praying. Ha!)

And we gaze on his Book.

There is the fool. A-sobbing on the carpet. Just the same as last time. And round him are Relieving Angels of the Day, their faces razed as with a veiling cloud, as with a razing cloud the Prophet is portrayed (upon him peace).

And prostrate in the living room, he can't remember which Naseeb he is. For there is a yearning spot to dash the Plan. To sacrifice the Game and go straight to the sunny Garden of cripples and pleasantry and fruits of doing Good.

And when the mother rises from sleep what will he say about the car?

That he knows? That he knows not? That the fault is his? That the fault is hers?

Tell her, we say.

Tell her, he's thinking.

We beg the fool as though the story could be different. As though the Pen changes course. (And it is the same if ye warn him or not. And his end is a world of shards that fly in all directions.)

But the mother shall rise and get ready in silence, and leave the car keys on the table. And leaving the car keys, take pushchair and Jonah to nursery. And he can't tell her. And her Protectors veil her eyes.

And again the *Ruh* dips a Wing in the wrinkled sea. And smoothes it unto a spotless plain.

And says to the Noble Scribes of the Left Hand, *And how did ye leave the slave?*

And I take my Pen that had been raised in case the churl repent...

But the Accounts of the Left Hand are already writ!

And what can describe his Account?

His sins scrawled in desert sands from horizon to horizon, endlessly drifting as dunes. And the desert whirls up as a sandstorm. And my letters of archaic *kufic* rise out of the desert as megalith stones. And the wind lashes the letters till they are honed into sphinx and longprowed dhows and beasts of burden.

But these forms are no more solid than the sands, they flow to other signs. For though the entries for the left hand be so many, this creature may still repent.

And I say to the archangel:

Surely the page is proven against him. And a Fire whose fuel is men and stones awaits.

And the *Ruh*:

And what if he were a saint? If you look but close enough, the good deeds of creatures dissolve as surely as the smoothness of skin gives way to corruption. And the bad deeds that soil the earth rise up as a rose. Look again.

And the wind blasted away the shape of sphinx and dhows and camels of the desert, and swept the sands away till it was an endlessly cracked plain. And in the cracked plain of calligraphy we saw him in the flat...

... a man beating his head against the carpet. His future vanished in a car.

And that slave calling on his phones. With no one awake.

The idiot going over and over who knew about his goods. Who knew about the car. Burning down his corridors of the damned.

And then he guesses it's the unpaid tickets; the council hirelings have come in their lorry, and the car is in the pound. And when he calls and gets it confirmed, he runs into the stairwell: *Jesus*, he weeps, *Please, Jesus*.

Every penny gone on Pakistan, fixers, the baggage guys. How will he get to Birmingham!

And Alif says to the Ruh, *Perhaps the creature is praying.*

But there the villien thinking, *I ain't crawling round their sh__ty manor.*

But that idiot reckoning Birmingham is too long to wait.

And he's thinking, *I'm gonna be shotting bags of tenners with the school truants.*

And what does Ali say in Birmingham when he answers?

—*Everyting oright? Tik hai?... Das right, das right... Him coming later, you know. Yah, him coming nex week... Make a praablem this week though, innit. Next week better... Why you want it now? Sometin happen, brodder?... Okay, no praablem. No praablem... Yah yah, we make it quick... You want to give him cheaper?... But Naseeb brodder, I say something: better you give it cheaper. Better you give it cheaper... Yah, twenty is better. But Naseeb, my share is same... my share is same. No prablem, but my share same...*

And I ask of the Ruh:

How does all this glorify Him?

And the Archangel traces a wing over the plain and releases an immense flood. And walls of water rise up as slowly as a moon, and at its zenith we read his actions in the streams of spume.

Look at him now, with Angels in succession, before and

behind him, and at his side, risking all to fly to Peegee's yard. For bridges had burned running to Pakistan. And there are twelve-year-olds ready to seize Your creature.

There he is at Peegee's yard with three hench on the landing with a crossbreed.

Come to straighten it out. Come to wheedle for cash. Come to call them to him.

The tall hench hauling back on the devil dog that takes dislike to Your slave.

Your creature cannot stutter it out:

—Nah, nah, Peegee, that s__t is all rinsed.

O Protectors, keep him close and evil far, say Alif and Hamza. And there the Angels in succession, before and behind, are spinning their shields.

The devil dog will make a lunge and Your creature jump as they laugh.

Don't show him you're chickens__t, they crow.

And the tall hench walk the devil dog straight at him on its hind legs. And abased, Your creature scrapes back down the wall.

For bridges had burned running to Pakistan. And there are twelve-year-olds ready to seize Your creature.

The towering walls of water collapse and are suddenly still.

We watch Naseeb in the skinless surface of a lake, his life trembling, trembling.

Hurry, wretch, hurry, says Alif. *It is already zuhr.*

There the creature takes a bus to the depot. Takes a bus to the pound.

If the Met Police are waiting for him still he goes to his fate like an idiot.

The latecomers hurry, hurry, to make timely their *Jummah* prayers. In the blessed month.

Take a step, idiot. He, Who takes ten steps towards you should you take one: He is waiting.

And outside the depot he'll take off his mujahedeen hat.

Behind the plateglass in the pound no one is listening.

His car key soaked with sweat.

Say, there is medicine in the boot.

Say, there are prosthetics in the boot.

But they'll need proof of disability. They want a letter from his organization.

There he is. A creature seized by invisible Protectors in such embrace he cannot breathe; a man pitched against a wall.

By the Time!

And the *Ruh* stretched thousandfold Wings. And a lozenge lake clouds over.

Ten billion Angels feel the fluctuations.

May ye glorify the Eternal Wisdom in the serene proportions of your hand, says the Ruh.

And with them we made ready to translate to the place of the creature. And the Relieving Angels return to keep a lozenge lake till the appointed time.

Two ripples pass along an Angel-shaped thread stretching from this world to that.

Did we even change the watch with the Angels in succession?

For it seems I have been keeping a lambent lake of calligraphy for ten thousand years. And for ten thousand years they have been making the *mi'raj* on a firebird-winged Burak.

And rigidly bound we vibrate as one with no delay...

4 | *The Account of the Angel of the Right Hand*

In which the Angels return to find the creature in his misfortunes; and with the help of friends and by the Will of Allah he continues in his misfortune; and he hurries to mend his fate: and he flees from his fate.

§

(Asr: 1603 GMT)

And Alif an Hamza hold a man in such embrace he cannot breathe.

Let it go, bruv. Let it go.

A yearning to dash da Plan. To sacrifice da Game an go strait to da sunny garden of cripples and doin Good. And Allah is *Adl*, Just.

And I rite one good deed.

And den sume next man from th depot comes out, a man like a *djinn* made o smokeless fire. And Yor fool croaks to him if he can just go get his wife's legs. Just get her legs.

And da man like a *djinn* looks at him.

Let it go, say da Followers.

As thoh ye can delay what comes by a breath, says Noble Atid.

Why, wots coming?

And next thing Naseeb is at da car pound where sume next man leads him thru da rows of cars.

And da creatur cant stop jabbering. The attendant thinks hes got a mental condition.

—I bin ther, boss. Peple walkin round Kabul with legs missing. Got girls wiv thir hands blown off cant wash thir doodah, scuse my French. I'm gonna take fifteen hundred of thez to Afghanistan.

(And each day I can record one good deed for his intention.)

The attendant opens up da carboot.

—Fifteen hundred of theze? Wha are they?

—Yeh-yeh, display products. Cast offs.

—What, an you just tag them on? Not much of a fit is it?

(He just wants to do good. Why is doing good so difficult?)

—Yeh, naah, but we can take this bad boy, rite, take this to India, an we can design like a Poundshop version.

—I thot its for yore wife.

(Ah, Jeff, you helpful soul—watch him! Tho his book of deeds

be ever so black. You can help.)

—Yes-yes. *This* one is for th wife.

And Noble Atid watches his neck vein pulse. Surely dey see his neck vein pulse!

Naseeb picks up de exquizite heft, the upper leg wiv da stash. Afraid it wud tumble out his Golden Fleece.

—Is that th one then?

Dat screw looks at him:

—Well what about th rest of it?

Yor creatur carrys out seven of da prosthetics.

And despair filled de universe as he waited on da pavement.

I pray You Lord, his heart beats, *Save this sad creatur, for I am f___d.*

We got yor back, brah, says Alif, Protector of the Rear, who now affects the sober wite *abaya* of a female Sufi. As tho Yor servants fate cud hasten or delay a hartbeat.

He waited on da pavement for his spar, wiv his limbs around his feet. His spar who'll drive him to a score.

I pray You Lord, his hart beats.

And Sonya pulled up in her Audi wiv his spar, and sez:

—O my daaays. Wot is that s__t!

And Yor creature cusses under his breth. And her hangdog Zach helps load da boot wid da legs an s__t. *(Zach, what you doin to me, spar? I got biznis to do. Cudnt yu get rid of her?)*

Say, da way to Willesden Green is hell.

And if you cud see da Caravans of Protectors poized on bonnets n hoods!—

Aw, we are breezin, cry Hamza n Alif, *Wet dat motor, girlfrend!*

Dat servant Sonia swearing down she cant believe dat Zach wud rope her into this, swearing down hes on one of his deals.

But Yor creatur is startin to jam his hype, Yor creature is feeling it, he's gonna be all rite.

—Dont say nu'in against da Afghans. We won da war for them goore. *Us Pathans girl. So now were helping ourselves.*

Dat servant swears down his unbelevable & Yr creatur starting to jam.

—You shud a met my legal. Yu ever hear of Boxer Revolution? You shud lissen, gel. Chinese Boxers, rite, they had a rebellion coz Britain yeah—dey're supplying em with opium. Yeah? An when dey rebelled—British, riht, they com and suppress it...

—And dats what got you lockt up?

—Gyaal is so jokes. Where you get her, Zak?

—Sonia! Sonia!

—Eh?

—Say it—just once. Sonee-ya?

—Sonia. All rite?

—Yeah, thats my name!

—Jus' sayin. Opium wars. Its history ain it? Little guy doz it, they bang em up without probable cauz. Queen Victora—she gets a medal.

(Tha creature Zak tracing tracks in his hair.)

—Hey wha you doin with my cuzin, geez? She use to stick with her own kind. Innit Son-ee-ya?

—Shut up.

—Dont be shy, Son-i-ya—you want me put in a word with uncle?

—Shut. Up.

Somwhere Willesden he sez:

—Wait up here.

And his book doz not delay or hasten.

And what can describe all da grains, all da graines of a dezert suspended in th storm?

And da Chopper bikes strewn outside a Dixy Chicken. And yungers inside wiv gyaldem. And olders pumping da bass in a Merc.

Each compassed by Receivers at th riht and left shoulders,

Protectors before n back. We are a Whisper at da believer's head, a whisper lost in th noize, heard worlds away. How strong our Powers!

Yor slave on his mobile:

—I'm meetin him now innit. This is it. I tole you yu shuda come in with me. Where you? We're just waiting for him to show.

And Sonya:

—I'm not waiting!

And Hamza: *Noble bredders, we gonna be buggin out tonite.* All thir Powers shining forth, th serchlite of thir eyes revolving. As if they cud deflect a grain of dust.

Da little hoodrats block th Dixys. And olders pumping up th bass in da Merc.

And Zak is geting looks. Your slave Naseeb nuff hype in da car.

—Is this one of yor deals!

—Chill. He owes me som dollars.

Dey jump when sume mouth rocks up from noware an bangs da bonnet. And for an instant I saw the agate eyes of Hamza under his Raiders hood and bustin trousers low.

—Wha you want blud?

—Nu'in, we jammin, sez Zak.

—You aint baying?

—No. Were waitin.

—Were not waiting, sez Sonia.

—You aint baying?

—Were just waiting, sez Yor slave.

—Wat you waitin for?

—Were not waiting!

—Edge up, bruv, we aint buying, sez Zak.

—Who you callin Bruv? says da Protecter of the Front, staring dem out under his Raiders hood, den wheels away sucking teef. An hes bowling it across da traffic:

—Well hurry up waitin, ain it! Befor I give you a ticket. They watch him bowl across da traffic, shoot his fingers in parting—*Boom*.

And Zak gon red:

—Looka dat chief, finking his all badman an dat. Yeh, go back to yr click.

And she:

—Wat are we waiting for?

—Wait up, sez Your slave.

He goz out an rocks up at th Dixys, staring down da lookouts.

—I'm not waiting!

And Yor slave yanks th door from da hoodrats, da hoodrats

blocking th Dixys:

—Scuse me boss.

All th Protecters rush ech other and are at a stand; as a variation of pressure or electrical or magnetic intensity. And da boat oscillates up an down.

As he eyes up the gash. They have no idea. How his vizion will be vindicated. An peple retributed.

Say, he waited in th Dixy for his man.

And his book doz not hasten or delay.

An his man parks up and nudges wiv da Merc crew, nudges wid da crew and dozent hurry; Your slave checks da creturs in the Audi, sees Sonya's perfect teeth as da radio whacks up:

Jinke sar ho ishq chaaon, Paon ki neeche jannat hogi...

And da Followers for Sonya n Zack join da song: *Chale chhaiyya chhaiyya chhaiyya chhaiyya...*

Wile a shadow wiv clownlike hair an a lether coat waits in da street.

And all da Followers flex thir shields at a bulletshapt fate, as if it makes a diffrence.

For somtimes it seems we trace words alredy writ. And his actions trace my words.

Read!

Dat creture Izzat is tapping da table wiv an envelop, Yor

creture watchin dat envelop.

—Deres peple wanna bang you out my frend. I herd you bin running yr mouth off alredy. Yore not in th game.

—Naw, naw boss.

—You wanna do bizniz le's do biznis. But you alredy giving me greef my frend.

—Izzy, Izzy, this is me.

All da Followers on road sheer across to th next man wiv his clownish hair—who lifts his arm n points at da windows, and thir shields point at da windows...

And next man sqweezes his gat...

Read!

And Hamza n Alif shear across da creture an wrap dere Powers around him.

Yr creture thawt a rock blew out da window, blew past Yor creture's ears. And a million splinters ar suspended in one world.

Den more shattering, and bare heads screeming. Everyone drops as s__t got bruck up.

He thot his man got cut. Allahu Akbar.

A sine wave singing in his ear. And peple bob or run out da door.

He saw that creture Izzat crease, in his hand dat envelop wiv da dosh—dat envelope belonged to him!

Yor slave looks around and reeched...

Thru da plateglass an its spider webs, dat servant Zack calls:

—Nassa, let's go!

The Followers pick up Yor creatur as th street rolls under his crepes; past all da Followers spinning *silat* moves, laying waste da Hi Street....

(Maghrib: 1757 GMT)

By da manifold Angels in da whip, watching over Your screeming slaves; we floor da clapping motor.

And Mikael of da wind an rack spred a hand across da sky dat expands and moves.

And th belevers hurry, hurry, to brake thir fast. In da blessed month.

This is the niht fortold in wich th worlds sing out; & for love of him th skyes ar turning.

Soon a deluge of angels brings down th Preservd Tablet to th relm a creaturs, and wiv them da soles of th beleving dead called down by *du'as*.

And Maalik, keeper of th gates of Hell, & his nineteen guards of da Fire. And seventy thozand Angels ech on seventy thozand ropes hawling da gates of Hell.

They rain down like da moving shelf of a waterfall and shear the atmosfere.

And th screeming cretures in da car; and Yor slave thinking, *They'll think I got him shot.* And Sonia banging da wheel swearing down hes unbelevable, & the dum one seying, *Slow down, slow down.*

Somware up the road they mite crash, & the pickny inherit a kilo of smack. And th Noble Scribe must stay his entry, for this creture may yet repent & pray.

And the Followers throw thir shield around. As if they could deflect his corse an atoms bredth.

Yah! Hawl to, Protectors! Lets speed him to his doom! Ya Seen! Ya Seen!

Thez drop Yor slave at th flat, and he sez, *Wait a minite,* the dumm one sez, *Maybe we shud get the car off rode.*

By the manifold Protecting Angels in Aleesha's flat, watching over th screeming cretures;

Dat slave tryin a sneek the other half a kilo of smack. Wile she's screwing about da car.

And dat mother coms with claws.

Hamza & Alif throwing tiger forms to protect him: *Dat wifey is gon!*

(Da Noble Scribe watches and shapes his Pen to the arcaic hand. But Atid must stay his entry, for dis creatur may yet repent or pray. For repentans erazes what happened befor.)

And da babby howling in th doorway.

5 | *The Night Journey*

In which the Angels bring down the Preserved Tablet; and the creature flees his fate; and reaches a station on his road; and he makes a *mi'raj* and sees a day of bliss; and is abandoned.

§

(Esha: 1944 GMT)

Da man runs out wiv a holdall.

And in dat niht as th souls desend, a lite blazed wirling from da house; dey rain down on wet tarmac.

And a deluj of angels brings down th Prezervd Tablit to th North Circuler.

And seventy thozand Angels ech on seventy thozand ropes hawling da gates of Hell to Birmingham.

And Angels of da morning Watch vibrate wid no delay.

Dey shape th Pen cut to *shikeste* style. To tell his story in finewebbd cursivs sweeping in tidal rinkles across da Book. Or in its airier form, suggesting mountins wiv bird n cliff flower vowels.

We copy da Book alredy writ, and write again. And therin no dout.

Da man runs out of da flat wiv a holdall. And his frends still waiting.

Dey fly th weeping gosts of Wembley.

And Yor servant Sonia banging da weel, and Yor creatur sayin, *Son, we can go to Dadi-Ma's,* and Zak saying, *Less just get dere.*

Somewar up da motaway they mite crash, and da pickny inherit a kilo of smack.

(Taraweeh: 2104 GMT)

By the last *juz* of Taraweeh.

By th faint muzak an the motaway as th door opens. By th schilds of th Followers and da silens of th Scribes.

And custumers in vacant corners, and Casheer at his counter.

And the intersecting Wings riffling other spectra.

Dere are Jinn in evry servise station.

Your creture tosses Rizlas n draw on da table and stares. And his mobile beeps another text from Aleesha.

That dumm one lookt down, his shaking leg. And Sonia grim. The Casheer looking on, the Caretaker of a qwiet life.

Yor creatur croking:

—Dont ask, man. I dunno. I jus turn up. Don't ask...

Motherfffff...

And Sonia:

—Its not yor falt? It's not yor falt!

Hes thinking, *They think I did it. Theyr gonna com looking for me. I am f___d.*

And when shes gon to th lobby he sez:

—Wot you bring her for, man?

And dat creture Zak mumbling she was helping.

—I didnt see Snow Wite bustin a gut for us befor. Gotta help ourselvz now. Gotta stick together.

Zack shaking his hed.

—Wot? Wot...! Trust me. I'm a better mate than some... Whas she doing?

There in th corner at da public fones—

—Wat she doing? We gotta go. Sort it out, geezer. Wat da hell you bring her for?

Dat servant clocks th dried scratches across Naseebs face, who fiddles wiv da sports bag, till she com back.

—Hey... Who were you calling?

And Sonia to Zak:

—You must be the only mug he can rope in any mor. Its like Im always trying to keep you strait.

And Naseeb gets in:

—Ain up to you, is it?

—No. Yore riht. Ain up to me... Its just I thot you were doing somthing with yorself, Zak.

And Naseeb gets in:

—Wot's it got to do with anything anyways? Hes not gonna be a brain surgen. Tchaa!

—Listen, I didnt ask what happend back ther.

—Whod you call?

That servant sez nuffink.

—Whynt you use yor fone?

—I didn ask what happend, but Im not going down for yore dumm s__t.

—O-oh shhh—

—If somone's hurt I want to know.

—Whynt yu call meat-wagon for me wile yr at it? O-oh Jesus...

And Your creeture hawls his bag shambling off for th bogs, he can hear her hammering Zak:

—You bin crawling round him like his som big oracle. Why you give a s__t?

Ther ar Jinn in every station toilet.

Da muzak piping into disabled bogs.

A pinch of skag cooks on foil until it runs. Da slave chasing da penging mettal wiv a straw—

—a hit of tundra winter in his lungs!

Left his bones to bleche somware, his trubles in a bin bag.

And his Protecters dissipate in da penging air.

His fone buzzing sumwere.

And a pure wite *buraq* stands with furled wings in th toilet.

And he saw himself sat against da toilet sistern, eyes red wiv da start of tears, his soul out on a flood of clemensy.

Across da false seeling, across da motaway n black fields, th Preservd Tablit broods.

And wat can describe da spase between th Book an ledden Earth? It seethz with bare soules sparking & annihalating ech other.

Truly his soul flots on benzene fumes. Mixt with pure n dross.

Truly it flots over da cafeterier, an da spectral viziters, and da creaturs Sonia an Zak who are saying:

—You gotta cut yor losses, hon. Befor its too late. I know you, Zak. Yu want to follow him down th toilet? Say, Goodby, good luck. Hav a nice life.

Yor servant Zak wanting to tell her, *Thats not how it works, not lik this, he owed him that.*

—Why? Hes not yore family, God help me.

—You wudnt bale on me.

She has to cloze her eyes.

All praize to th *Ruh* that desends from the Everlasting Place, smelling of da sherbert of hooris, and visits wid vizions:

The *burak* spreds his wings and bows, so dat th slave may mownt, and yea, in his salaam—

da slave dismounts in Peshawar!

And have you seen a mujahid Naseeb, walking past the old house with its buntings and signs? And a one-legged Dada tapping his donkey with a switch; who clasps his hand: *You got something for me, little uncle?

Naseeb from far away: Come back tomorrow, mate...

Do you see the border village on the white dirt road? And the boy with the goats slips something into his hand; the servant murmuring: Safe, little bro...

And the orange poppy fields around. The men with their curved daggers: *Naseeb sabib! It looks good!

And his regal hand.

Your creature oversees a Volkswagon caravanette loaded with cement and lime by PeeGee with his fingers missing and a couple of boys. A tea crate on the ground and PeeGee turns to him: You want us load this one, boss?

And the caravanette driven by the beanpole chief with his devil dog hogging the passenger window and Naseeb crosslegged on the back side-seats.

And do you see the building site by the parched road? Foundations dug, men in dirty kurtas and turbans shovel cement and rubble or drainage. Iron struts sprout out of truncated cement pillars. And the creature stands at the signboard: Under Construction— HAZRET MD. RASHID ALI KHAN HOSPTAL CENTER.

*Sahib, we brought the generator current by running a line over that hill.

Good, man.

A call flung from a minivan whips away on the dry air: *Naseeb bhai—it looks good! And a ghostly handwave from the window... Abba!*

Abba?

And for a moment of Allah's Mercy, the servant's heart squeezed by love... ready to give up the kingship.

And walking through the bazaar, the men in jumma kurtas, admiring the Russian weaponry. A one-eyed man nudging knuckles.

The old farmer and jute-wrapped crate on his back, works

through the crowd and salaams Naseeb; and your creature returning it, and nodding to the boy hanging back with the pack horse. Your creature calls for the stall owner, the Afridi with black moustache, to inspect the box.

And he pats the scraggy packhorse with the face of a mufti. And in that salaam a tundra blast—

and da slave dismounts in da toilet, and he hits da foil agen.

And my Noble Scribe Atid picks up da Pen but must stay his hand.

And can I rite som merit attaches to his miraj?

Yor man rocks up at the counter mashd.

Do yu see the dumm one Zak at da food counter? Wiv da Casheer cleening tables.

The creature Zak pretends he dozent see him. But Yor slave hes givin it hes got no dosh, an nodding at da counter...

Naseeb rocks up at da table. And dat creature Sonia almost smiles and ignors his acrid breth. And he slides into his seat. His Followers etiolated into nat's water.

—You speke to Dadi-ma?

—Yeah, we shud hed, he sez.

—You alrite?

—I'm all rite still. You all rite?

And after a wile he sez:

—I admire you, ya know.

—Me? Why?

—O-oh. You know wha you want... Going collige. S good. Don't loze it.

—You wer doing stuff befor.

And even mashed he came on aggy.

—Wot you mean?

—Just—you didnt always mess up. You musta done collige.

—I lernt. In nick. Mongst other places. I gotta get out of this.

—So what were yu in for? Mugging old ladys?

—Ah, sume bulls__t I got don for one time. We was regular teef, innit.

—Whos *we*?

That slave grins weary.

—Yu know, you can help him, *bhaiya*. You can be more of a frend. If yu left him alone.

(And Noble Atid notes his lip curl.)

They watch Zak mongin at th food counter.

—Yeeh? An wat do you want? You staying Tottnham forever?

—Im going Uni.

—Yeeh? Well, Zak aint gonna be ther, is he?

—His got his own life to sort out.

Yor slave looks to say she can't bulls__t him. And over at Zak checkin out his chips. And da cashier propa neek.

—Looka dat. Typical Paki.

She looks unsure at da Cashier an Zack.

—F__k that, he sez. I'm not ending up like tha.

—Wha are you ending up like?

And he's all:

—Oh I dunno, I dunno, Son... Its not spose to be like this.

—Look, if it wasnt yor falt, why cant we just tell them?

—I cant go Five-O!

—Im asking can you be strait?

And Zak cumes steeling in, & slides in wiv his sossiges n chips.

And da strip lihting vibrates wid da souls of *Laylatul Qadr*. They hum along a thred dat connects to thir kin. And what can discry the soles of belevers?

Som mystics imagin th pure metal of a singing bowl,

overtones blooming on da folding air, da patterns of marigold rose magnolea exstaticly shook.

—Its up to you, Naz. Yu want me to take yu to Dadi-ma?

—Dont take me.

Yor creatur teks a handful a fries & drops them in his mouth. And his eyelids shimmer wiv da shape of souls under th strip lites. He nearly tips over.

And he sez to Zak:

—But hole ting, bwoy, its a mistake, rite! Soon as we go ma main man... sort da hole deal, smoo-oth as yo gel's ass.

And she:

—Smooth as yore hairy ass, boy, when yor frends fry it! He sees th flickering souls under his lids, and creeses at her ire.

—You orta smack some respeck into yo woman.

And now the dumm one:

—Shu'up, man.

—It's up to you. Do yu want Zak to end up like you?

—Whas up to me?

(My Noble Atid watches and reherses da Pen to th salient fetures, simplifying an shading a passige, dat the Account acheeve harmony; his *kufic* shorn of vowels & lexical markers, da bare letters sailing a watery mirrer.)

—Heh. You know me an Zak rob dis pussyhole once.

Yeah. Int that riht Zak? Polish or summat. So we get stoppt, you remember? An he's got all the geezers forren notes on him. Tcha...

That creatur Zak's face burned. Your creeture rockd his chaire som more.

—Yeh. Had to say I give it him. They let him go—did me insted.

And her Protecters fall thru her stomack. And in th dumm one his Protecters thrash.

—Well maybe yu wudnt have to if yu didnt get him involved.

—Oh, its my falt? Ri-iite. Ffff__ksake. You think hes so innosent. Tcha.

—Hes trying!

—It's my influens. Like he aint got a brain or anyfin.

And th dumb one:

—Shu'up bout me! And you!

—Who woke you up?

—Shu'up man! Wot you givin me all this grefe for? We're tryn to help! You still givin it th big G, like I'm yor likkle boy— who cares about yor shtupid—I wudna done half the s__t if it wasnt for you! I got my own plans.

—Is it? Wat are yoo gonna be then, Tupac?

—Not *yoo*!

—Is it.

Yor slave grabs Zaks jackit with one hand, Yor slave grabs Zak and lungez in his pockets. And wrestels out the packets of choclat, biskit, muffin, and wrestels out da muffins, crisps n ketchup, and tosst them on da table.

And da Casheer lookt across.

And dat creeture never took her eyes off th dumm one. As Yor slav crows at him:

—Whassis? Whassis s__t? Is this my c__p or yorrn? Wat is it?

That creeture Zak swares at him and tris to keep da pile around his plate.

And she:

—Zak... What you doing?

—Looka it. F__king master criminal! Hah! Na, man— dont blame it all on me... Yeh. You start seeing da pictur, gel?

—I see da pictur, boy.

—Yeah? Whassa pictur, ma woman?

—I see da real pictur—Mistah Big Time bent over in prizon gettin servised by few *goore* boys, innit.

—You need to open yor eyes, ya know—das yorr problem.

—Too much Bigtime—das yorr problem! Too much bigtime willy an no vasline in da ho-ole prizon, baby!

An she pick up her keys:

—Zak, you gonna wake up and find me long gon.

Your slave gon all begfrend wiv Zak now:

—What you sniffin round my cuzin for anyways? Eh? She ain interested in yoo.

The slave calls after her as she scrapes:

—Got other plans. Innit, Son-i-a!

Dat creture Zak still picking up the c__p, dat creatur eyeballing Yor man.

—Wha? I'm just saying, innit? We dont need yor *poonani*, bway.

And da Cashier comes to wipe a table.

And Zak goz to scrape:

—I aint your boy.

—Hey... Hey, Zak. I don't mene it. I dont *mene* it. I cant have yoo on my back. Not yoo.

Dat creture givs him a look to say, *Wy not?*

Yor slave stares after him a wile. Da Cashier looking nervus at da mess on th table.

—Wha? Wha? Yu want us to go? Whassup, Charly—we look lik criminals?

Yor slave picks up his bag an slopes.

—Keep the change.

Da Cashier left to his visiters and solitary jinn.

And Noble Atid: *Is he not th muther of his fate?*

And th Protector Hamza: *Hes a mutha all riht.*

By th last niht of *taraweeh*.

By th faint muzak n da motorway. By th schields of da Folowers an th silens of th Scribes.

He fownd his arms & legs in th car park.

6 | *The Night of Power*

In which the Decrees and the Angels and believing dead descend; and Your creature's fate is rescued by his friends; and he is taken to his kin where he finds peace; and he leaves and goes to an old haunt but finds no one.

§

By the pressure of angels in the swagging lowest heaven, and heavyclouded Mikail.

Across the motorway and black fields, a Night of Power broods.

And what can describe a Night of Power?

When the gates of Heaven are opened, and the gates of Hell are closed and all the devils shackled. And the believing souls descend.

And at the fiat of the Ruh a thousand angels brought down the Preserved Tablet.

And I saw Mikail flicker in electric storm, and stretch Wings bounding the geometry of this world.

Read! That your Lord who knows the fall of a sparrow's egg has measured the fate of every soul suspended between Heaven and

Hell... And Allah is Merciful, All-Knowing.

Ah, what can describe the Preserved Tablet?

It is a raincloud of endless drops endlessly falling. (If the raindrops endlessly fall then they are endlessly suspended, and we fly in their grey sea and they will never splash our face.)

And we scry the creature's face in the lake. There in his eyes four shadows wobbling in skeins of light, as he drowned in a scumstained bath. The water yammering in his ears. Then their shapes explode in shards.

(Laylatul Qadr: 2059 GMT)

The Followers emerg to rap thin chill arond Yr slave in th car park.

Where were you's? sez my Noble Scribe. *Have you com to protect him from th drizzel?*

And th Followers Hamza n Alif:

Ware was wee? Ware was you Noble Scribes wen he was a baby chewing electric plugs! Yeh, ware waz yoo when we got him to coff up a safety pin! We was dere from th begining!

Da Followers emerg to rap thin chill around Yr slave. Dey assume th semblans of cortiers from Samarkand, in flowing green n turbans.

His artificiel limms in a pile at his feet, da kilos in his holdall, the univers points at Naseeb, as he calls his Ali *chaccha*:

—I need to come now, boss.

Thou Your creatur got by in Urdu, his chaccha spekes in English:

—Why you coming now? Restarant is open. Better u com tomaarra. Tomaara come.

(Yr slave can see him on the phone stroking his mustach thinking, *Why this idiot mekin a praablem for me?*)

—But restarant vaary bizy, my frend... Him not coming. Selim him not coming. Maybe Mondy come... Vaary difficalt, my fre-end. Why u need it tooday? Everytink orriyht...? But Naseeb, mek a prablem forr me innit.

(And Your creture can see him wiv a toothpick winkle absant minded.)

—No, no, I fix it, yarr. I fix it, no problem. But we shud it make it diffrant share... Hahn. Eyou understand, my brodder? We shud make da share diffrant. Make it shaare diffrent, innit.

And dat creture clicks his tonge and gets louder:

—No, no, I helping *yoo!* This make a big hedacke for me... No, but Naseeb, dat one is beforr share. Dat one is beforr share. Now is diffrent innit... I understand, I understand. But now I helping morre...

And wat can describ the Decrees re-tuning the cord of evry soul?

—I'm a bisznes man, chacha. Aint nu'in dodgy. Yore a biziness man, I'm a bizniz man. You wanna do bizinz, le's do bizniz. But you gotta stick to th script! Aint me changing da script... Da story, chaccha! Da story! This aint gonna help! I didnt risk ten yeres for-for-for—

Whil Ali picks his teeth:

—Orite, orite my frend. You dont worry. I see vat I can do. Yah-yah, I see vat I can do. Tomaara, no prablem. You coming today? No praablem.

And Yor creture knos his stroking his mustach saying, *This idiot make a big hedacke for me innit. I dont no why he makin a big hedacke.*

His artificial limms in a pile at his feet, Yr creature didnt kno how long he was stood. His life swirls round dis plughole.

BAILIFFS due to remove your GOODS. Call NEWKEY on 01604 100341 to stop this.

(An immens churning of fat hevens, dat twists into seperat cyclones down into ech created idiot.)

But hedlihts flash & a car rolls towards him and th mist coyling in th hedbeems. And he cant see.

Then da creatur Sonia rolls her winnder down:

—Ile take you to *Dadi-ma's*.

And wen he doznt move she sez:

—Im not having yu get us in truble. Ile take yu to *Dadi*.

When Yor creture finally got in da back he sez:

—Yu can drop me nerest station.

—That doznt help.

An his dumm spar turns:

—This aint my idea to pick yu up.

Then Zak he doznt look agen.

Across da motaway and black fields, th Prezervd Tablit broods. It rains bare soles an angels in falling phosfer.

Da Followers for Naseeb at his hed n back, dere Wings still crumpld in glassy slivvers, Yr slave bugging out tryin a cotch: Leesha n her twenty messages, Zak an his pussyole feelings, Ali askin to get banged out, street fam he rolled wiv giving air, like he was a thirty-yer-old wastman. Truly, all he rememberd was beets n ugliness. Th time he was a player only reminded he was ownd: a jarring clappin jokerman. An older beeched on silt.

Say, why cudn he remember happiness?

Dat servant Sonia saw him rolling up a zoot and switcht: *No!*

And Alif says: *Yeah she waznt saying no last time.*

Dat servant saw him rolling up a zoot and switcht.

And Yor slave thinking, *Yeah she wernt saying no last time. So what? They all com to me. Same as I give them nice wite lawyers. Like them horible daddys girls crawlin up at som Ladbrok-s__ting-Grove party—Hey, man, yorr byeutifull. Can you fix me up?*

Falling into that endles black well.

Wandering coridors of th dammd.

And Hamza: *We gonna be burning til he crashes.*

Say, a dred is desending.

And from its wings drip jeweled rain. And da drops run raggid corses & sheer acros da windscreen. And for an instant dey splatter da *thuluth* hand of his Book, befor da wipers wipe dem clene, and flow agen as sines.

And da cuts on his face ware Leesha had scratcht out her angwish wer hurting for her. Tho she was nuff hype in da flat, an hed had to prize her off his back, he was hurting for her.

And wen dat creatur rung he ansers. And tawking to her he cud perhaps find out he wasnt dead.

—Leesh.

Yor servant hears fumbling, then Jonah showting like *Waaow,* & more fumbling & whispring. And she was probbly on th carpet wiv Jonah gettin him to say: *Naawib, Naaawib.*

—Say, *How are you, Naweeb?*

—Naaawib.

—Yu arite Jonah?

—*Ar you feeling better?* Tell him Jonah.

And her child presst a button an med it sqwawk.

—Say, *Ar yu feeling better, Naweeb?*

And th child:

—Heehn?

—Wha you doing, litle bro? Arnt yu in bed yet?

And da servants Sonya n Zac hadnt spoke. But dey listen th way we's listening.

—Say it Jonah, *Were waiting for yu to com back. When ar yu coming back, Nassu?*

—Wenwa comee ba, Nannu?

—Ile be back soon. Why you up so late?

—Heehn?

And I rite the cretures words: *Why ar yu up so late? Why's he up so late, Leesh?*

—Nannuu!

—Tell him, *Are yu alriiite?* No yu tel him Jonah.

Coz she was wiped out, and cudnt take her pills, and culdn trust herself to tawk.

—Nanuu, arla aw wy. Arla aw wy.

And I rite his words as one good deed: *No worrys, dude. Im going to bring u back a present.* Do you see, Noble Scribe?

And shes saying:

—Say, *Ar you going to bring back my car?*

And th cuts ware she had scratcht out her angwish wer hurting for her.

Allah, let me bring back her car.

—Arna, brim ma ca-aar. Arna, brim ma ca-aar.

—As soon as I get back, Jonah.

—*Why did yu go so qwickly?* Say, *Why—did—you—go?*

—Haanh?

—I had to go, litle bro.

—Brim me-me ca-aar.

—Say, *Why cudnt you stay a litle bit?*

—Laters, I gotta go.

And she started crying.

—*Mummy's worrid about you.* Say, *You shud have stayd a bit. Were worrid about you.*

—Deyr not gonna come nocking. Alriht? Ile let you kno—

—*Mummys worrid abot you.* Say it, Jonah—

—I just walkt into sume beef. Theyre not after me. I got to go littil dude.

—Heehn?

—Say, *Mummy wants... Mummy... wants...*

And Yr servant let her cry.

The lihtes of the souls streme; ten thozand brakelite eyes of hell wind into the unseen landscap, ten thozand headlihts of angels flow to London; dey streme double-banded thru his hed.

He dremes speed cameras & police lihts were going off behind his hed, the electrical storm jitter on th sky;

they streme unwavering thru his head...

The soul dreams of fireballs.

The old family living room opening onto an esplanade, and he fancied climate change approaching: a lightning bolt hit the old Rotunda building on the Roman hilltop of Birmingham centre. Another lightning strike loosens the city scarp, and buildings tumble in a slow wave. The soul imagined all below the city centre lay in the path of the avalanche.

He was on the phone to tell his mother. Then the avalanche reached their home and he saw a boulder of fire roll down his mountain to mow straight through the house. More quaint fireballs roll towards him and he faces them like firey pace bowling—letting a snorter bounce in front of the excavated walls and leaning out the way...

When Your servant awoke it teks a wile before he realizd it wasnt real and he has nothing heroic to tell.

And they saw da blinking red eye of da GPO tower.

And th shroud of Mikael reflecting agenst th nite sky.

And Yr servant gided Sonia to th redbricks of Alum Rock. And baer pillars of lihte stand on th street. Bare pillars of liht.

And a plain of praying angels rolls from Ward End to Small Heeth.

And dey stop atside the terace hous, & tiny wall & crissanthemums; da motor still running.

Den th frends turn rownd. And Yr servant nods.

Then Zach offers to bump. And Naseeb nudges hesitant. Dem both surprised.

—Lets goo in, Your servant sez.

—We better head.

—Nah, cume, man.

—Yeah, we better go, Naz, sez de other servant.

—Nah, cuz. We gotta go in. You gotta see *Dadi*.

But Sonia hasnt seen her for time and she wasnt dresst. But Yor servant was begging it & his Pathan etiqett all coming out.

—Le's go. Just sit for a bit innit. Theyll be realy happy to see yu. It'll mek em happy.

And thoz frends Sonia an Zak keep looking at eche other.

—Theyr not even going to be up, she sez.

—What you on about? Theyr alwiys up. Theyr alwiys cooking in case sumone coms at one a clock. Its Ramzaan! *Dadi's* gonna be so happy shes alwiys asking bout yoo.

Dat creture Zak meking his noizes:

—Yor family just want to see yoo Nassa.

—Yorll be helping me out. Look like I got respectabl frends.

And he goos on n on and after a bit she switches off the engin.

Your servent's *Dadi* rapt in wite cloth ansered th door after da third ring. Wivout missing a beet she sez:

—*Walaykum salaam, hav you come? Arifs not back yet. Whos this?*

The frends Sonia & Zak hanging back on da pavment.

—*Dont you remember London chachas big girl?*

—*Who? O-oh, bhaisap's girl is it?*

And in that niht as th souls desend, a lite blazed wirling from th hous; & da casett resites Quran.

We fan into corners of th downstars rooms knockt thru & filld with chunky sofas, wardrobes, an a single bed with prayr mat.

And what can describ a Niht of Decrees, when angels crowd da places a men?

And plates of onion bhajji n samosas on da table.

—*Did you see your mother? Whats Sheela-memsahib doing? Whats the matter with your face? Were you in a fiht? Oh, beta, what's happend to yur face?*

And heeting up meet dishes, his *bhabi* tinkling in brite *lengha* & hedscarf & arms of braselets; and Yor servant bizied to bring mor dishes n drinks.

(And I note seven merits—do you see?)

And da grandmotha neeling on her prayr mat & bed, wif her Quran & *tasbih*, an made her neece sit close.

*Yaa, wat is that yore wearing? Tut. Is yor mother all riht?
—*Jee, Dadi.*

—**Your father, brothers? Acha. Give my salaams to them. Ask them to pray for me, my health is not good. Yaallah, who's to say?*

She turns to Yr servent with his pet name:

—**Ey, Jahan, this man is who?*

Yor creatur gooz, *Hes not Pakistani, he doznt speke Urdu*, and she sez *Oh* and left him alone.

—**What are you doing*, she asks Sonia.
—I'm studying, Dadi.

—**What are you studying? Jaow, then study. Have yu made*

namaz? Chi, how can you make namaz in that? Are you fasting?

And Your creture looks at Sonia. Coz he forgot it was Ramazan.

And she sez:

—No, Dadi. Were *musafir*. Were traveling.

—*Yore not keeping rooza? This nihte? This last nihte?*

—Yeh, sez Yor servant, not nowing what nite it is. Is it toniht?

—*Yore not keeping Laylatul Qadr?*

—No. Yeh, yeh.

—*It will be good for you*, she sez, looking at Sonia.

—Were traveling, sez Yor servant.

—*What travel? Jurney to America. Jorney to the moon. Still keep namaz. Ey, girl, don't you rede namaz anymore? Hehn?*

—Jee, Dadi. Im... Im...

And the elder catches on she mite be more than just *musafir*, (Oo-oh), lamenting anyway:

—*Hie reh hie, your mother broht you up with such troble. And now yung people let it go. Just dance and galivant.*

And Sonia grins and prest her nees together.

—*Arent you going to eat? Will he eat?*

Dat elder got up n slaps a chairback with an old hand and calls to Zak as if he was a dog.

—Oy! Oh *beta*. Hoh, you eating? No eating?

His *Dadi* badgers them to the table. And th *bhabi* swishes in an out & keeps the kitchin.

—You eeting *murgh*? Eating *murghi*? Eating chicen dis?

And Zak:

—Yes, aunty, *shukran*. It looks very nice.

—*Does he eat chicken*, she asks.

—Here, Sonia, take this. Tek some of this.

Yor servant servs from his seet, and bosses Zak:

—Here, eat, man.

The *bhabi* come in with another dish, and swishis out onder her shawl. And keeps the kitchin door, her gold bling tinkling, and he chivvys:

—*Bhabi. What you doing? Come. Sit down an eat.*

She mumbls an he gooz:

—*Come here. Sit. And eat.* Go out or come in. Dont be hangin about, woman.

His Dadi asked about the Old House, his other *Dada*, little *Dadi*, how Wais and his wife were. And rambles about an uncle who sent his wife home but da father-in-law returnd her. Your servant cudnt keep up but he kept grunting he new.

—*Pray as much as you can tonit for yr father.*

(And at th word, da shadows of kin ripple into th room;

da faders & moders and stilborn & thoz taken gently: as elastic deformacion, or variasian in preshur, or potencial, or temparatur; and if you look closly enuf at da angels in th room they doo not sum up to 180°.)

And she sez:

—*Is he staying?*

And th frend Zak checking wiv Sonia:

—Ive got to hed. *Shukran, antie, I have to go.*

And his Dadi iritably:

—*Is he staying?*

—Acha. Err. We cant stay, Dadi.

—*Whats this yore saying, beta?*

—I've got to see *Little chacha.*

—*What for? Then see him. Stay. What's the problem? Ho, girl, you stay.*

—Weve got to head back, *Ammi,* sez Sonia.

—*What is this yore saying! Yore not staying? Ey, Jahan, arnt you staying?*

—I just have to see Ali *chacha.*

—*What is this you're saying, you lot! You're not praying toniht? Yallah, girl! Stay. This niht you won't find the like. Quran sharif seys thos who rede and pray this nite its worth ten thosand months. All yor sins will be forgiven. Thos who pray all will be granted. Ey, lissen beti, if you give dua toniht for yor Dada-Dadi, Allah wil lisen. So many blessings. Tonite all the soles of the deceesed vizit: if you pray toniht the sole of Jahans father will find blessing. Yor Dada-Dadi will find blesing.*

When Arif rocks up in his kurta an wastecot, da shadows of thir kin dey ripple in th room.

And what can describ da Decrees?

An he giv a smile to Sonia that brakes wider:

—Salamalaykum. How you been? Bin a long time! Uncle all riht? Antie? Ware you staying?

—Im just giving Naseeb a lift becuz his car broke down. And his frend.

And Arif sed, *Oh*, and past strait to his wife wiv a bag of shopping.

And da bruvvers havnt lookt at ech other.

—*Arnt you eating*, sez thir Dadi.

—I'll eat later, seys Arif.

—*Eat. Together eet.*

And da cassett tape snapt to the end. And its hard to ete till Arif goos upstars to change.

Protecters vibrate wiv thir creaturs, in th sad walls of his *Baba's* hous.

—Here, Zak, tek som *dal.* Tek some *dal,* man, dont insult

my fokes.

—*Let him take wat he likes*, sez his Dadi.

Naseeb spooning it past Zaks hand:

—Joker is half ded, nuffin but bone. They don't feed em in Neesden. *Hes been fasting all day.*

And thiyr drinking *chaa* when Arif com down. And da brothers had ta look at eche other. (And th Followers n souls ar walls of standing waves.)

And Yor servant to his brother:

—Why dont you eat?

—I heard yu went back home.

Yor servant give sume kind a shrug.

—Why didn you tell anyone? Ey?

—You shud eat sumthing.

—What you go for?

Noble Atid sees, that creture's look lik *What bizness is it of yorrs.* And the frends feel it.

—Just we had some papers to do for the land. Or arnt you botherd?

—You shud eat sumething, Yr creture warns.

—Ile eat when Im redy.

And thier Dadi:

—*Eat a little.*

—All that prayins gona be hard work.

—Wharid you say!

—Just... tonite. All the praying...

(Stay yor hand Noble Atid.)

—What wud yoo kno!

—*Acha, Arif, peple have come. You shod be happy. Such a nite.

—I dinn come to make troble, *bhaisap*.

—Obviusly not. What troble yoo ever make?

—*Acha, Arif! Leeve it. Its not done.*

But Arif:

—Yoo dont want troble. You put yorself out when Dad died?

—*Its not riht. This is supposd to be a niht of forgivness. Take Allah's name—*

And Your servant coms back:

—Yore talking? Yorr talking—!

—*Speke with Allah's name.*

—You call to see how Mom was?

Sonia saying *Bhaisap* but nobody hears.

—Oh! Shes *yorr* Mom! Yore gona look after her? You did such a good job with Dad...

Thier *Dadi* teks small steps to th kitchin, now old.

—*People shod respect Ramzaan. Whats the point of fasting? Fear Allah.

Your servant shaky:

—Ask yerself if you put yorself out.

—What?

—Ask yorself that. Before you start talking.

—Yore a dissgrace!

And Your creatur gets up to go: and his frend Zak gets up.

—*I dont want to disturb. I'll go. Dadi. I'm going.

—Why dont you kill her too!

—Ask yerself if you were a brother.

—What!

—When I's inside.

We urge da servant as thou th story can be difrent! As thouh da Pen changes corse.

Shuffling to th door, picking up his bits, & choking up:

—Yeah, ask yerself...

—I dont want a-a-a brother like yoo!

—I'm going, Dadi.

—I havnt got a brother!

—*This nite, such a niht, such a sin. You two dont understand. Peple forgive, send blessings, send prayrs. Ya ghafural raheem!

And Sonia rose mortifyed, to take a blessing on her hed,

and say, *Salaam alikum Dadi.*

—**Acha, my dear, my salaams to bhaisap and bhabi. Tell them to send thir duas. Hie reh hie, such a sin. Say* namaz, *girl. Ho! Say* namaz. *And tell Jahan to call me. Tell him. Acha,* Allah hafiz.

And from da kitchen door, da *Bhabi* bid Salaam.

And da servant Zak mumbls somfhing on his way out.

And when da frends get to th car, dey see Yor creeture bombin down th street with his bag.

—Nassa *bhai*, yuve left yor legs, she calls.

And he sez:

—You ware them.

By the gleem of past drizzle on niht streets.

His lif drifts by as weeping vellum.

And wat is his lif?

A hawl a sardines dat switch direcsiuns, ech one flashing blankly left & rite, yes & no. Eche tyme th creature crosses da rode its world forks off to good n bad. And we wil never find our way bak.

His lif drifts by as weeping velum, kufic redlaid an gold.

And da Protectors assume da semblans of Janissary soljers, wiv da baggy pants an bork hat; dey march to th drum of *mehter.*

And seventy thozend anjels on seventy thozend ropes

hawling da Hell thru Bordsley Green.

Do ye see da street lihts dripping *rahmat* wid dere halos of spun shugar? And da fingers of liht arking from his lashes;

And if hed a lookt up for a sec hed a seen da hart-shaped face of th Ruh as a bride, as a bare-armed maiden & lofty tiara & a hen party trailing by; and her bridsmaids song trailing by: *This is the niht fortold in wich the worlds sing out; & for love of him the skys are turning;*

But yer slave dint see none of it, burning dan his corriders a woe.

And wen he wakes his feet a taken him to the old taxi place basicly, an like the same cuples outside; & it slaps him across a face & he gets a swet on:

Here he is. Same as last time. He cud see th dog runing dan th street n looking bak;

Lookin at the frosted winnders, trying to fink why he shud goo in.

And his thinking, *I ent going back there.*

And hes got the gold brick dust in his bag an all.

But the resterant was saying *Ali hes not in*, & Ali's mobile wern picking up eether.

Befor he reckons, *Wot if hes tryin ta shaft me. I gotta get backup.* An he thinks das what hes cume for.

And th Followers vail his eyes & his stinging fice.

And sum next manz on th control desk thees days; an baisicly doznt know jack, but he knows Shaka thoh.

And Yer creatur gooz up the tiht creking stars;

waer th standing waves of anjels & of soules ripple in th walls: *Welcum O secret of Quran, Welcum O cherishd frend!*

& in the bare room deres nufin, egcept a creture in her bra & knikers handcuft to the raidiater. And her Protectors dissipated.

We fan into corners ware th dogs did bleed into th florbords.

And the walls of angels sing: *I am yor Love, yr solace, the hert yoo strive to pollish;*

Da handcufft creture, her rolling eye cud almost see us.

Yr slave he dunt know wha to say he pretends to look aroand for Shaks an says to her: *Orrihte?*

The handcuft creeture in her bra & knikers & her cobbld back bent over. And her rolling oye cud almost see us.

And the walls of angels: *You are the mirrer to my imag, yoo are the miraj...*

And he looks in the tilet & rubbish room, coz he dozent know what to say, so he sez to her gormless lik:

—Have yu seen Shaka? Ja know if Raj is coming?

But hers smackd out of her tree.

And seventy thasand vails must he lift bifore His beuty he will see.

And when she storts moning as if hes goona lamp her, his bloods gooz cold. An he daint know what to do so he hangs abowt; still he dozent want to be gawping at the bruzes on her leg like.

And Yor creatur leves becoz he got a bad feeling hes goin to do sumthing. Do somthing stupid. An he yad the gold brick dust in his bag an all.

And peraps I write a merit.

By the saules in whom Allah is plezed, and thoze whoz heorts ar further sealed. And eche step further astray.

And da creture who driffs dan Coventry Road reckless.

An he cud stil see th dog runing dan the street an looking bak at him.

And Yor creatur thinking maybe he can call the cops anonymus for her.

(And I wryt seven merits.)

7 | *The Night of Decrees*

In which Your creature takes refuge and prays; and is visited by friends and strangers and given guidance; and he goes to his fate and is guided by his Uncle; and he rejects guidance and accepts his fate.

§

(Qiyam: 0051 GMT)

And Yore creatur driffs down th Cuventry Rode.

An if anywon had a past us theyda sin Yor man wif a mom & her sprogs in th blessed niht; with Noble Atid in burka pushing me in a pushchar, and Alif and Hamza with Star Wars wands o fluuressent violit slashing the nihgt:

But Yor servant dint see non of it.

And the restront sez, *His not here.*

But have yu seen bare Muslims, out in ther kurtas and bomber jackets? Cuming or going fro *I'tikaf* in Small Heeth.

Ware the howses got nokked thru into a moqs. And a lyhte blazed whirling.

The ranks of Ayngels, the atomwinggd & the thozandwingd, crowding the spaces o Heafens & da places o men, wif da prayers of the beleeving Jinn & men.

Yor creatur relized he was gooing to the moqs.

And Yor Lord is Gracios, *Kareem*.

And Yr creteure waches dese uprite folke atside. The yunguns in skull caps, an da serius repenters wiv beards & the *Dadas* in tanktops tottering on sticks.

An he goos up the carpet stares in his socks, seeking the place of wudhu, ech passige pulsing wif atomwingd & thosandwingd.

And the Follwers wishpering, *Why not pray? Why not?*

And da man: *Why not pray?*

(I write dat th servant seeks Allah. While th Pen only follers da writ.)

Say, he is glad to make *wudhu*. Sitting at th taps between them, & dat bag riding his back.

And in da middel of da *jumma* hall a white Burak spreds his wings; wif waves of angils in acts of adoracion, singin stonding neeling prostrating;

And when he goz in da jumma hall he chucks his bag o gold to the wall, glad to find his spot on the empty spases of da corpet, & remember what he cud of *namaz* & *Fatiha*.

And three Djinn were sitting arand da Burak and arxing:
Whare do all the engels cume fram? Doo they wait in heafen

for eche soul? What hapens when he dies?

And the Burak saying:

What do yu mene?

(So many Djinn, so many Angels! crowding da space o belevers wiv interfeering liht.)

And Yor man he remembrs wat he cud of *Fatiha* & *Iklass*.

And when his face kisses the carpet weave it ripples wif da kin:

Whats gooing on Allah? Can ya let me have just this one? I now its not halal, but Im tryin a do somthing.

And he remembrs wat he cud of *Fatiha* & *Naas*.

And when his fice kisses th carpet the weeve bicame his fader dedd on the hosptle bed.

Its lik yure alwiys trying to hold me back. Is that how ye want me? Im on me kneees, look. Am I supose to be this? I need this, Boss. Blatant. It int fair.

And I saw his fice turn to me (*Walaikum salaam, noble cretere*) and to my Noble Scribe, who salaams & bows to th man.

The mans eyes clozd—as thoh he weren another created Muslim who werships himself. (Doo I not deliht in a grain a *du'a*, made as I am of Allahs *zaat*?)

And I look a his hands in *du'a*, an I see wha the cloze eys of the beleever cant—the lambent *thuluth* letters traced on his paams, an shyning on his face. Dese marching standards & Alifs tippt like spearheds, & the consonantal shapes so meny scimiters.

And Dad. I forgot yu. Whered yu go? Can ya help me? Can ye look after us? I dunno Dad. There musta bin sumthing yu wanted to give me. I dont blame you. Wat ye want me to say?

And the carpet weeve bicam th face of his fader dedd on the hosptle bed.

He thinks he sees sumwun in a grup, with a shaven hed & a fistful a beard. Familiar & changd. But Yr servent gooz sumware els in th moqs, with a wall for his woe.

And den sume time a stripling from *Tablighi Jamaat* sits down in front a Naseeb to put him riht wile he was down. And Your servant cudnt get de woman in her knikers out of his hed, wile da stripling coos with his thin voyce and wiskers:

—So Brodher Naasib, mor prac-tical efforts. Are ther more prac-tical efforts?

(And Protectors nodding sagely.)

—I use to pray *Shabarat* as well, for Baba.

—Father is pass away reecintly? No. Then this is meritorius in normal *salat* and *du'a*. But we shold not make miss-take, Brohder Naasib, to follow un-nessessery prac-tiss. Un-nessacery belief, Bro-dher Naasib, that doors are open for decese person on this day. But *hamdulillah* we are here to explain peple. Pracc-ticel efforts, Brodher Naasib, to do all *farz*, and folow the *sunnah* of Beloved Profete *sallalahi wassalam*.

And da creture cudnt get da smack sitting at th bak wall out of his hed.

And he sez hes goona pray for his Abba at da back.

And th Protecters assume da semblans of th litl Bangladeshi kids messing at da bak. And one a da rownd litl kids reminds him of Dilly dimpeld & moonfast in Goa.

And he reckons probbly the woman in knikers theyr just messing, shel be alrite probbly.

And Dilly wiv de aggat eyes gets talking to Yr servant & aks if he cums to th moqs, and Yr man sez he was here for his Dads *janaza*. And the other one with magnezium eyes goz, Did yoo bery him? And the Dilly kid elbows the other wun who seys Soz, but Yr servent sez, *Me and my brother*.

And sleep was overtaking em all & his brest is accing when th boy rubs his topi sleepily across his hed, da servant wants to put an arm arond & draw him near.

And he shut his eys and driffs off an he doznt hear da protecting yungers:

We kept yow from the sharp ecge when yu fell, an took the safty pin out yr gob, an we just want yu to know yu mite be a gormless teef & never hav a proper job in yr lif, but yoo broht us joy. Cauz noble ruh, we knew you was soft as shii—

Subhanallah, sez Atid.

And sume may be graced wif da Presens of the Ruh, and some wif da rosewater of the Prophet in sleep...

The people straggle in from a plain, to a ferry or riverboat churning; perhaps an evacuation, but Your servant was a happy follower. And two fighter pilot buddies exchange pleasantries and then, as the plain dried up into sand, they took their leave to go up and strafe them from the air.

And he saw the lines of gunfire bursting the sand—that seemed drawn to a red plate by his side. Each time the plane circled another approach, Your servant picked up the Frisbee plate and held it aside to draw the fire. The pilot smiled apologetically and the servant had a friendly chat. One of the soldiers dug in with a grenade; the plane came down with bullets deflecting off his helmeted hand. And Your servant tries to lob a softnosed grenade and sees it foul off his own elbow—and a second later it explodes...

He was sleeping lihtly cuz when his arm was tuched he was awake:

—Salaamalaykum aroit bro. Long time, Naseeb.

(And all the Protecters at peac.)

Yr servant took the hand profered as the famelier sat biside him (and with a pang he saw the Dilly yungers gon):

—Long time yeh yeh! Thoht I saw yoo. *Maashaallah,* good to see you in the masjid.

—I didnt recgnize yew. Whappen Jojo?

—Yunus, bro, Yunus. Yah-man, I aint tha anymore, yeh yeh. I bin bless, bruv—bin a jurney, found the *siratal mustaqeem.* Im Yunus now, *hamdulillah.* But you got ther befor me, *maashaallah, maashaallah.*

Hes tapping Naseeb on the chest & rocking back & forth. (Bifore Yur servant realizes his tapping his Sord of Ali T-shirt.)

That creatur chuntering about messd up times at da minicabs *astaugfirullah*: as if *salaah* wiped it clene th dogfihts & th slags from th care home. And Yr servant wunders if he cud tell him abot da handcuft woman.

—But Allah taks ten steps twards us if wee tek won innit. Even a black man. Na, man, I beleve thez things ar ment, Allah *subhaantaala* waches everything.

Yor creatur nodding.

There was th pure place agen, clenzed of human greesiness. Envying the uplifted loozer Jojo. Beaten by life into goodness. He wants to be beeten too. To giv up being in th Game.

And the carpet a rinkeld sea of calligrafy and da beleving djinn & angjils rippling to th horizon. And standing bowing prostrating, dey articulate the fleeting *ayat* of his Book; and thoze human *mu'takif* rocking on a rinkled green sea, as sphinx & longprowd *dhows* & beests o burden...

But dese forms are no mor solid than da sands, they flow to other sines. (And if ye look but closly enoufh, the good deeds o cretuers disolve as shurly as da smoovness of skin givs way to dezert.)

And his lif teks the shap of a falling wave.

Envying the uplifted loozer Jojo. Beaten by life into goodness. Hee wants to be beeten too. To give up beeing in th Game.

But he woz in the Game. And wihle others found simple *sharia*, his was to sacrifise eezy ways, and deal wif da ratf__ks of *dunya*, da way the Profhet struggeld agenst th backstabbers & venal, to benefit others.

(*Can you bend yor Pen agaens his will*, seys da Noble Scribe.)

And hes wundering if he shud tell him abot th woman.

Tha familyar Yunus pulld Yor slave off to another prayr room hes gotta meet somwun (and wiv a pang hes sin dat the Dilly yungers are gon).

A litle knot of bruthas on da corpet, da same denim trowzes an salwars hitchd up thir calfs, & *kopi* skull caps, dey acnowlidge Yunus wordlesly.

—Go on, ask him anything.

Dere's an awkward scattering of da last *mu'takif* teken from thir *du'as*; & da brodhers smirking. Theyr round a fair man waring a zipup & Uzbek hat, crossleggd & upriht. He seems taller dan anywune els.

—Ask him, theyr cajoling.

Yur creture sits down wif Yunus.

Sumwone mumbling if its allowd to ask *du'a* in prostrashion—

—Anything. Ask him anything.

Yor creture carn understand who da stranger is or why the audiens. And while they dither, a questiun rancles in his hert agen. Da four angels who cum down to th newborn—one to confer long or short life, one to say rich or poor, one to say when he'l die, & one whether he'l end up in Heofen or Hell...

So if the angel came down and rote No faith, then wots this big charade on erth? Wats Allah doing giving this baby no iman, and all th warnings gonna go sshhvvitt over his hed? And at the end what? Hes gonna fry him in eternity becuse He alredy condemnd him? Whassat all abot!

(*Fry yoo mofo losers*, crow da Folloewrs.)

And da fair man in de Uzbek hat smiling crossleggd & upriht.

Bifore it becume unbareabl, somwone asks:

—Can broder say how we know wen to prey in th North? In the north places whare the sun doz, go down.

That stranger smiling, an wiv even gaze & mien he explans how *azhan* is calcualated thoh nihtfall never falls, how the *umma* is maintaind. The kind of dumbs__t that put him off in th first place. How did this even matter?

And de brofers scanning da mizrable audiens for the next questiun. But Yr creture's alredy ansering in his hed.

I am responseble? Im not the one most responseble. I'm a speck a dust. Gods the one Who knows all. The one Who made us outta this crap. Made me weke, put me in the game and sed, If yoo play well you will shair Paradice, and if you play bad I'll fry yuo alive. I never ax to play this game.

And da Protectors: *Braaaap!*

And da man felt one of his fones vibrat and turn his stomac.

And when he ansers his Chaccha's seying: *Yoo cuming brodder? You bring it* mishti?

And in da street the serriyd ranks fal down, wif wands of fluuresent violet slashing th dark. And Angils write the decrees & float da vellum down th drains weeping red & blak.

Dis niht coverd by Mikail of sheltering cloud. Pregnant wif all past and futur. Full of gaps & full of lihtes. Yea, and da baerers of da Throne, de keepers of da Tablet, and da sefenty thozend ranks o sefenty thuzand angels hauling here de Infernal place.

And it took half an hour to walk to Lahore.

And de Protectors assume da semblans of Janissary soljers.

And da *Ruh* as a pressure, or electikal intensity, sefen hundred leegs wide. And we saw Israfil in gorgus flowing green and turban, the rams horn razed & his lips presst. And wat can desribe da blast dat cracks the graves? It is an iron mote that swells to convulss da worlds.

And Hamza: *Todays the day, bway! Redistribute sum welth. Mak em pay! Trust us. Yoo da Man!*

An it took half an our to walk to Lahore.

Da Folowers, protectiv, deflect his foot from wonky flagstons.

And Yr slav he was affrayd. Of lozing all.

And der was a fere, *Is any of it real?*

And most of the other Baltis wer shut. But otside da Lahore Yor slav sees sume wite blokes trying to blag dere way in, dere shirtsleefs & dere eyes of smokeles fire. And da Protecters assume da semblans o white blokes trying to blag thir way in.

And th door was shut, & a new waiters waving him away until he mowths his here to see Ali.

And den Mani cums an opens up, and Yr servant gets da creeps thinking of dat slav & the slags from th care home. Wile the blokes wif eerie eyes are gooin, *Whys hee gooin in then?*

And thers still a cuple finishing thir drinks. And the angils & souls still crowd da place of men: a singing bowl wave that cwivers & convulses crisanthemum rose magnolya. And dat servent Ali's at the conter counting takings to the twang of Indian muzak. And Maani joins him to pick his teeth till th stragglers leev.

—Salaam, how ya doin, *chaccha*?

Tha servent Ali cums out & embrases him three times:

—Walaikumsalaam, yunngg maan. Good, man. You have truble?

—Na, boss. Biznis good? Yore roling in it!

—Not bad, not bad.

Theyr tapping at the winder, da yung waiter shaks his hand, *Sorry, sir. Clozed.* The Protecters are tapping at da winder.

—You want anyting? Anyting? Take a seet.

That servent Ali smiling, looking once at da bag, an he gooz bak to to the takings.

—I ate like. Realy. I was at Abba's. I was at Dadi's. We all set?

—She oll roiht? Arif all roiht? Have someting. Yah yah. Anyting, *beta*. Have *rasmallai*.

Truly, da niht takings cum befor his deal.

Yor slav's looking for syns that tings wer set. Deres another Asian wiv grey hair & a gut at a table.

—Whoz that?

—Dat just my frend.

And his *Chacha* dozen say nowt else.

Da new waiter saw out da last pair. And da lads are still otside:

—Mate, we just want a take-out.

—Aar, I'm starving. You must hav summat like.

—Sorry sir, oven is off. Chef hee clene everyting.

—Come on, ar kid. We dont care if its cold. Wer'll pay extra.

—Wer'll pay duble! Wha ever yuve got.

So finaly wen Ali's cashed up:

—*Maani! Give them take-out if they pay duble. Tell chef.* Hello, saar! You paay it dubble, okay! Das roiht, das roit!

Yr slave's skin hes almost crawling wiv insult & paranoya as dey let da wite blokes clump past to th conter an empty dere pokets. And the agate & magnezium & da grins of da Folowers fuzed in thir half-shirts:

—I was reddy to def it.

And da slave Ali leevs them to Mani & went over to his frend. And he moshions Naseeb to another table:

—Take a seat. Him an me just talking lik. Okay?

Yor slave cums closer:

—Whats happning?

—*You broht the mishti?*

—Wots going on?

—*Is it in your bag?*

—Wheres Selim?

—Naseeb, brodder, batter I say, you leaf it item heere and I fix aaverything for you. Batter this. One, tow days, aaverything is fixed—good pris, brodder, good pris, belief me.

Yor creture cud hear the clubbers at the conter wif Mani: *Yer a lif saver mate.*

And Yor creetur:

—I'm not leaving s__t here.

—*Yah, better you leve item, trust me, bhaisap, I can fix better prise. Becoz you dont kno, Naseeb, I know deses pepol.* They see you and they becom crafty, I kno.

Yor creture rasping:

—Wheres Selim?

—Selim him not com.

And da aggate eyes of da clubbers looking over at them, Yor slave thinking of Ali & th slags from da care home, Yr slave staers at Ali till he cud speke.

Afraid of th way his *Chachas* face bicome his ded father's. Yr slave staers at Ali till he cud speke.

—You an me need to talk.

—Das roight, das roight. We talk wan minite, my frand. But I say yu honest, brodder, I fix aa-veryting far you.

And da whit geezers aggat eys, da whit geezers smyling over at him.

—Im waitin in the back for yoo, sez Yr creture.

—Yah-yah. Das roiht. Anyting you want, yoo tell chef.

And in the kichen tha creature Ghulam the chef his shirt was stained with tumerik;

and the angils & souls still crowd da sealing: eech a singing bowl shaking space to a frenzid wave.

And in the kichen tha creature Ghulam, the chef his shirt stained with tumerik, and tha creature Raks, dat wiry street sort— thems interupted from clening the oven & storing food; thems opening tubs o chiken & foiled tandoori to blast da micrawave.

Da Protecters flex Powers across da kichen walls, dey

wishper to Naseeb: *You gonna get moved to. Yuo aint even tooled up.*

And Yeor creature pacing fury. And Ghulam says stuff like *Boss, what you bin up to?* But Yeor creatur pacing fury.

Then Ghulam doin his nut at Raks:

—Look what dis *bainc__d* doing! Raks!

And Ghulams wrestling Raks whos bending to spit on the nan breads.

—*Let me go. Let me go. These bainc__ds cume in last month. Theyr goin to find a speciel taste from my ars.*

And Yr creatur's thinking, *Im goona get moved to. I ain even got a borer.*

The order gooz out, & the staff clean the kichen.

And we note Yr creatur dayn find a chance to slip a borer under his jacket.

& Raks hes off, & Ghulam hes taking off the giant pot o currybase for tomorrer. And Ali cums in chewing *paan*:

(And da Scrybes & Folowers & da Souls and the angels in sucseshion are standing wavs, for the Decree is in our Pens. Durst we rede it? *Lets give him the good news,* sez Alif.)

—Yass my frrend.

—Wot ar you playing at?

—Now Naseeb. You now me.

—What the f__ks going on! Yoo tole me you had it set.

You fink Im just gonna give it up for som poppadams?

—You naw me.

—If you ain interested just tell me. Coz I got others who are.

The smile on dat elders lips becume thinner.

—You vant do bisiness sumwone else?

—I got no chice now, have I?

—Is it.

—This ain uncle-nefhew s__t. This is bizines!

—Is it. Okay. Then you give my shear.

—Yor wot!

—Yah, you give me my shar!

—I give you jack s__t! For wat!

His oncle gooz to the sink to spit out *paan*. And Ghulam his shirt stained tumerick looks on cold. And his uncle sez:

—Yah, yoo chenging story, my frand. Yah, but you chenging story. You tink yu can do it bisnez widhout me?

Yor cretures hand on da bag shook. Da bulls__t was happening.

—I was dooing you a faver!

—Yoo doing me favor? How you find it dem? Hah? How you do bisinez widout me? Yoo tink you find it peple in Pakistan? You think yoo find it in aarport?

—I cudve done it blindfold!

—Mos be crazy. Mos be crazy. No, no, no. You changing story, my frand. You give me half.

—Yoo lying sack o—! Four grand we sez! You forgetting? Four grand or twenty percent. Wichever one—

—No four-percent-twenty-percent! No! You give me haff share!

Yor cretures hand on da bag shook. Th bulls__t was happening.

—Or give it me *mishti*.

—I give it? I give it d-d-dan the drain before I give it yoo! And Ghulam guz all bored:

—Dont be a dick.

—Who arksd yoo, shortarse!

And Ali:

—Dont make trobble.

—Whar are yoo gonna do abat it!

And dat cretur Ghulam:

—Werr'l take it if we want.

And Raks da wiry sort is ther at th door. And Alif and Hamza shear to ther man & throw thir sheeld around.

And Yor man keeps his sholders hihg thogh hes shook, & gooz to Ghulam:

—Who yuo talking to? I know yor games. You forgetting? Yee-ah, I aint one of yr underage slags. Kno whaam saying? I aint the one got sumthing to loose.

And he looks at dat creture Ali:

—Int that rihgt, *Chaccha*?

And his uncle & Ghulam dere eyes goo dead & dere muoth a hard line.

—Eyou making bigg misstake, says Ali.

And he blunders past, Yeor creature blunders past, th Protecters slamming blind shields. And his *chaccha* & goons only half goo to stop him, & his tears protect him.

And his oncle after him:

—Dont mak trobble.

And otside angels roll back th plain of prayr, ware they camped from Stoney Lane to Stratford Rode.

Yor slave storks into the dark, da clewless niht—

Whisperers cume, his mind twists sudden panics.

What if he took it? Gave half, took half—deres still a qwarter kilo sitting uncut at Leeshas. Twelfe grand. Ten Gs even... Just to get out of da hole.

The Folowers wihspering, *Def it, mate. You shud flush it down the drain bifore yu give it him!*

And Yeor creature:

What is that? What kind of snake turns its own? You looking dan Dad? This is yorr cozen! You left me to this s__t-eeting cockroch?

Ten grand? Did it even clear his detts? For what? What wud he have!

What abat da plan, Nazza, da plan? Put down a marker. Yer own crew. Enoufh to sit wif da big boys. Den bild the empire of legs & hands & rahmat for amputees and recompens for mujahadeen.

The Folowers whispering, *Def it, Naz. You shud flush it dan the drain bifore yu give it him!*

Wishperers come & turn da servant's hart. And th Protecktors cum and turn his hert.

If I had a shooter. If I had a shooter...

And the soles returning to Heofen—they now as much abot dis world as a cod nows a forest fyre. (Compard wif da first Heofen, everything in dis world, even the interior of stars, is baerly abov zero).

Yor servant folows his feet: he is hurrying to da woman on da radiater. His got a feeling hes gonna do sumthing. By the soles in whom Allah is plezed!

And wen Ali calls on da last bar of his fone he sticks it on silent.

And I mark seventy merits!

How longs it take to Bordsly Green? How many events

in th passige of a sigh from da slave? We too along wif da creture suspended between Heofen & Hell.

Here he is the old taxi place. Same as last time. He cud see th dog runing dan th street n looking bak;

And Yr creatur goos up the tiht creking staers; waer da standing waves still ripple:

& in the bare room deres nufink.

Yor creture's hand on his bag shook. Da bulls__t was happening.

Yr slave he din know what to do.

And he looks in the tilet & rubbish room for her. But deres nufink.

And when he hears da footsteps thumping up the stars his blood gooz cold.

—Oi, bossman! I herd you was here. What yew bin up to? Bin yonks.

And Shaka cumes & gives him knucles, & gooing *Yeah-yeah, What yu doing thez days*, like he can smell somthing in it for him.

—I got biznes.

—Wif Ali like?

—Na, this int smalltime s__t.

—Serius?

& hes gooing *Yeah-yeah, Just let us now if you want a links,* like he can smell somthing in it for him.

—Wot happend to that woman in here?

And that cretur Shaka starts pulling a face starts gooing like, Na, I waznt here mate. And he says he'll com back up.

And Yor man shambles in th room lik.

Why cudnt he remember happines thez days? Screwfaces had twisted s__t till he cudnt walk into a yard wivout snickering hench n bottom feeders playing him.

And Ali's bin calling the last bar of his fone.

And Yer mans thinking his gonna do somfhink.

And he calls his mom.

But he cant get the number rihte, and his fone gooz dedd.

And he heres da thumping up th stiars:

—Hey, boss, I got a call from Ali! He must now yore here.

And dat slav Shaka is holding out his fone:

And Yeor cretures going like *Tell him to f__k off,* but dat slayvs saying *Yoo tell him.*

—*Mister Rashid. You varry toffh guy. You know dat? Yeh. Like eyour Dad. Varry toufh.*

—Whaddya want?

—You knaw me, Naseeb. Yeu my bhaisap's blood, ennit. Beliebe me, peple ask me Pleese Ali sahib, take fifty parcent, take sixty share—just we do bisnes. Ennit? Coz dey know, Ali sahib, he fix eevryting like. But Naseeb brodder, you want aall, I give yu. Just you tell me what yu want. Coz yeu my bhaisaps son, ennit?

And the servant pacing de room, ware the dogs bled into the florbords, & a hundred unwanted things being offerd.

—So you comin ennit, bhai.

—For what?

—Henh?

—What for?

—We helping ennit. We help ech other like.

—You havnt got anywune lined up.

—Yah. Selim him come. Selim him come. Yah.

After a wile, wif Ali pestering if hed got da *mishti*, after a wil Naseeb gooz *He's there riht now?*

—Yah, Selim here.

—Wid the money?

—Wid money, yah. Him come.

—Selim is ther, roiht now? Wid the cash.

—Cash money! So you comin ennit? We fix eevrytin.

—Howd he get the cash so cwick?

—Yah, no problam. No problam.

—How did he get the cash so cwick?

—I give some. Som cash I give it. Eyou understand,

Naseeb brodder?

—How much?

—*Who?

—How much cash money?

—*Seven tousand.

—Its twenty.

—Das roiht, das roiht, no prablem.

—Yoo got twenty grand?

—We give it twenty, das roight.

—No! You got twenty Gs, rihgt now?

—We hab!

His fate holding the phone. And we are wif da cretur suspended bitween Heofen & Hell.

If I had a blammer, if I had a blammer.

—Hello? Yah, yoo toufh bogger, you naw dat? Your Dad, when he lose it temper with me, ya naw, werry tougfh bogger.

And in and out of Urdu:

—*I would s__t on the spot.* You remember whan we buy it eyour Latif Nanas land? When yous is littel. *We all went. Nerly ate a bullet, me. You remember? Hello, bhai!*

—Yeah.

—Eyeu like yor Dad. *Naseeb, son. Jast yoo, Selim, me. Alone. Alrite? Just we. Soo you bringing merchandis? You have it, beta? Bhai, you bringing merchandise?*

Yor slave holding da phone. Shaka waitn lik a prick.

And Noble Atid:

Suerly the Decree is pruved against him. Suerely aronde his neck a yoke up to his chin. And a barrier befor him and a barrier behind, and a vail acros his oeys.

And in da street the Angil of the Soor wif the horn presst to his lips.

The seventy leags of Mikael reflecting purpul from the lihgts of da city.

By the returning soals raining up in stremes of phosfor pulsing blew & pink;

By the angil-shapd threds that bare string the spase betwin heofen & erth;

they roll back the plaine o prayr from Stony Lane to Stratferd Rode, sefenty thuzand engels & seofenty thazand more bound for the much atended haus.

Doo ye see da street lihtgs dripping *rahmat* with ther halos o spun shugar?

And *Jibreel* wif heort-shapd face & loftie tiarra leeding the angils of da Throne throhg the streets, and sefenty thuzand engels & seofenty thazand more bownd for de much atended haus:

Ye are created to write the book alredy writ, & therin no dout. And Allah is mercifull, all-knowing.

Now his feet wuld show the way thruh this forest. Or fall to robbers and wulfes.

Can I trust you? Can I trust you, Allah? Im here init. I'm here. Got no choice. Howd it all get so on top? Abba, if yore watchin over me, keep me out of greef. Just do the best for me.

And it took haf an our to walk to Lahore. And Yr slav he thinks he sees Ali at da window, and he goz ruond da block.

Im heere. Are You therr? Why arn You heere Allah? Yore everyware els.

Except Pakistan, says Alif, & spins an cracks hir tunic sleeves.

Braaap, gooz Hamza.

By de gleme of mizzle.

The slave gooz rownd agan. The nihgt dezerted. Da resteront dezerted.

Inside wud he find if God cared.

And waitin engels throw dere shadews across from da restront, ware across from de resteront it coud a bin Raks an Ghulam hanging.

Hee had no blammer, no backup, and the streets dezerted.

When he taps on th glass door of da resterant it wold

happen the way it happend.

Assalaamu alaaykumm brroodder, seys dat slave in his rumbling vice, an his eyez fliker to the bag. And deres nowon arond.

And Yor cretures lyf taks the shape of a falling wave. And the wallpaper a rwinkled sea of calligrafy.

—We can go upstare, brodder.

And Yr servant gets da creeps thinking of dat slav & da slags from th care home.

Turn back. Go forwerd.

The man gooz to the kicchen—

And the Protectors assume da garms of *silat* fihters, busting tyger forms in dere baggy *salwar* and *keris* blades;

And in the kicchen Ali is breezin agan:

—But him getting cash ennit. Him getting cash.

—Wot, he's gone to a f__king cash mashine?

—Not cahs maschine. From nodder man, ennit. Lot of money, my frend. You think yoo just take out? They keep record, ennit.

—Ar yoo playing me! Arr you? Coz if hes not here in two minites Im gonn!

—Him yor same blood, ennit. Selim him yor same blood. We yeor dads blood ennit.

—He aint my blood. I dont trust oither o yew.

—Ya, him my son. Same is like yoo, ennit.

Yor cretur hears da front door play two notes as it opens.

And Yoer man knew hee was lost.

And da Protecters thraw tyger forms and slash de ayre wif *keris* daggers. As if it deflects a flye.

And Naseeb lets him goo into the resturant, to let in Selim or whoever.

And he heares bare heeds, & Yor man knew he was lost.

He casts araond to hide da bag. This handful of dearnesse. And da backdoor was deddlockt.

And thers more vices, *Is he in ther?* And da man he jumps when he heares Selim bark, *Are you in therr?*

Yorr creatur casts arond to hide it: *Jesus*, he weeps, *Plese Jesus*. A cretur seezed in such embrase he cannot breethe; a man picht aganst de oven.

And dere was a yeorning spot, to sacrifyce da Game & goo strait to sunny gardens o cripples & doing good.

And he teks out a blak polythene parsel. A handful o deereness. He cast arond to hide it: & Naseeb his taking off the giant pot o currybase for tomorrer.

The folowers deflect his finger from da nife.

Da man teks off the giant pot o currybase for tomorrer;

in his hand a black polythen parcel, that tumbles uot his Golden Flees, gilding his face wif blyss. O shynyng faces o da blesst!

I pray You Lord, for I am f___d. Ameen.

They found him wif a kichen knif.

And hwat can descrybe da Protetcters dat crowd da plases o men? Eche an opposing sine wave canceling oute to silens.

Dey found him wif a kitchin knif. And Ghulam says:

—What yu got ther?

—Hes chopping onnions innit, sez Raks.

—Yoo making *jalfrezi*? You making it for us?

—*Eyuo got oure goods?*

—Whars the stuff then?

—*It's in bag. Him bring it in bag*, seys Ali.

—Whaers the bag, mate?

By the manifold engels wacching Yeor screeming slaves.

And what can discrybe Decrees ree-tuning the cord of every soale?

An immens churning of fat hevens, that twists into separat scyclones down into ech created idiot.

They tek him down wid a broomstik & macheti.

(Hamza throwing tiger forms & Alif dooing dragon, dey slash the ayre wif *keris* swordes & draw da name of Ali.)

They took him down wif a broomstik an macheti.

And Yeor man got knoct the spark out.

Hes falling back inside his hed, a blac bottomles bed, wif all the stars & the dazzling dark of heovens...

He was in a brick-and-tin shack, squeezed between Abba and Arif and the menfolk at some alchemy with a barrel of burning tar; a hurricane lamp darkens shadows. Ghulam the chef in filthy vest and scarf, ladling the mix with the silent watchers, chadors covering mouths.

Chef lowers a thermometer in for a reading.

—*Tik hai, dear hearts?

—*Give it more.

—*It's strong enough.

—*Blow their heads off.

And someone with a white plastic container pouring into the drum. Abba holds them around the chin as the boys try to sneak a look. And Arif gives a spiteful shove—he nearly touches the scum-scaled metal, the firewood scorching his face. And Abba barks, and presses him back in the crush till he can't move.

Da hood was cold & smooth, & bare arms scweezing, & muffled water rushing.

Deyve took him down wif a broomstik & macheti, & teken him upstars.

We gather in junk rooms bounsing wiv rats. We gader in a bathroom steyned with sins o neglect, & we look in a heort-shaped lac, & dredd is falling from the tap, the color of p__s.

And rond his neck a yoke, an a barrier befor & behind, an a vail across his oeyes.

And wen Yor man cume to, he thinks hes upstars in th taxi place, hwere th dogges bleed into florbords.

Da hood on his hed now hot & smooth. He reckens its a bin liner. & when dey lamp him lihts goo flashing inside da pitch, & da bag crackles.

—*Dont keep hitting him, idiot. He not gonna be awake.

—Bhenc__d, if hes stuck it up his a__e I sware I'll stick my fist up it.

An sefenty thuzand engels crowd a bin bag, dey bow to da man, an sing o the lihgt of profhetes on his brow.

He wants to say its okay, hees surrendered. They can kick him to kingdom cume, meks na diffrence.

—Yoo wanna f__k wif us?

He rekons its a bin liner. Evry time they bang, a flashbulb gooz off inside th bag & sumwone inside exhales, the flash suckt back to a brihgt point. And his head singing, singing.

The bag cumes off thrusting him into th blinding bathroom staind wif da sins o neglect. And dredd is rorring from th tap.

Say, they hawl him to the seething bath. And his Protectors seeze the sides of da bath. And dredd is rarring from da tap, it runs raggid corses across da scummy sides.

And for ane instant it spatters tha *thuluth* hand of his Book, as swirling standards & simitars & behedded diacritics, & speeres pointing to da One Truth.

And Noble Atid:

—*May we trace the beutie of thees ayat in da sereen proporciouns of his beshitten lif.*

—*Ameen.*

Say, the Protectors seeze da sides o da bath, *Yaa Seen! Ya Seen!*

But dem hench they tip him under water. The shock burning down his sinuses & gob.

There in his oyes we see ouer shadders wobbling in skeens o lihgt, as he drowns in a scumstaynd bath. The water yammering in his ears.

We dive in to a boiling lac. It seethes wif *ayat* sparking & anihilating eche other. And shear along de seashell coclea of his inner ear, ware the spiral dampening is deffened by waters, and

Hamza & Alif cansel out de wihspers of Shaytan.

Bang away bways, it dont mene jack, coz I surrender.

Then bliss cume to Yr man, an he cud see mandem wobbling on the surfis waves, & pink snot drifting, & he gnew hes tippd up in th bath.

Concussion buoyed him on oceans.
He thought they held his mobile to his ear...
—*Hey, Jahan.*
A voice slow in solid sea, he couldnt tell if its Arif:
—Haraamzada, *why you run off like that? You alright,* mate?
—*Im alright still. How you?*
—*Where you? Let me come pick you up wherever.*
—*Ah, its all right.*
—*Come, man, its Eid innit.*
—*I cant get away bruv.*
—*Why didn't you let us know where you was? We was* worried.
—*Im alright still.*
He could see four shadows on the bobbing loops of light.
—*We been worried about you, Nassa. Say, We been worried...*
—*That you Leesha?*

—*Say, When you coming home?*

—*Waah wa comee haoom.*

—*What you doing, bro? Arent you in bed yet?*

—*Say, Were waiting for you to come back. When are you coming back, Nassu?*

—*Wenwa comee ba, Nannu?*

—*Whys he up so late, Leesh?*

—*You want me to keep your legs?*

—*My what?*

—*Wenwa comee ba?*

—*Your legs and s__t.*

—*Nannuu!*

—*I'll keep them for you.*

And his soul went out on a flood of clemency, this breaking sea of love. He couldn't bring the shadows forward, but there was the ache of his mother's eau de toilette, and lacing fingers through his hair...

—thier shaps shatter into dancing globuls as a fist brakes de surfise, & Yr man got dragged uot of the bludy bath, into da green liht deffened by choking, dey smac up his heed;

& da Protectors surging owt they grip da sides of da bath & whirl da sweord of Ali:

Ya Seen! Ya Seen!

And in the rat-bes__tten doorway wif a door that didn cloze, a pure hwit buraq wid da face of a man flexes florid wings. The pur hwite buraq waches as dey batter Yr man;

Ta Ha! Ta Ha!

and dey crac his heod agenst th tap bifore he goos under agin & th Protectors let go da craven body.

We look on a raging see of signes, they loop & weave de water (an if ye look agin ye see his lif lic the shap of an eddy):

his mother talking with a roomful of men...

... a dog smeared in excrement and blood, on three legs...

... an umbrella smashed in his face...

We look on a raging sae of signes, his ende in ten billion drops.

And dem hench have tippt him under water. And just for a sec he cumes to, an he sees ouer shadders wobbling in skeins o lihgt, as dey kick da s__t outt of him in a scumstaynd bath.

And on the ecge of da bath stand seventi thusand scrybes

dat start to rwite bare sheets, to write baer sheets & thraw hem in a blizzard o leaves, & clogg da wateres wiv ragges.

And the taps are moning lic a beest, an da Horn of Israfil blasts thrugh the bes__tten pipes in da hause, an pimple da sweying waters of da bath.

A yeorning for de Heofens calls us—an angil-shapt thraed that pulls us into th gyre.

We dive into a churn of pink blud.

And in his oyes we are holding him down in a scumstayned bath.

Sume mysticks make de *mi'raj* of an thuozand yeares in blink of an oye, & clime a ladder of subtile liht on Buraq, ontil they cume unto a lote tree in da Sevendth Heofen; beyonde hwich Gods glorie tourns to ash.

An sume folde the geometri o this world to that, & dyve into a craetures brest bane.

(And dat *Buraq* may look upon a penging room o swingers, baer heds swinging in a penging room, an knaw as much abote this world as a cod nows da forest fyre.)

Wee dyve into the lofts of his lunges; as far as wee looc de branching coral swaying wid de surge, dat floods with evil braeth.

We flie on dat *Buraq* with the face of Yr man, whare de red cells & platelets rush, unto de Paradyce of his heort;

in the valted chambers of da well buzy haus, baer engels hammer de walls wif *Hayy!*

And Alif & Hamza rwap a shield arond da hyping heort, & cry, *Hawl to, Protectors! Allahu Akbar!*

A fist cum & rip the shaking skin of waters. They drag him up & his jerking lunges dey spew themselvs to burst.

—Yu think we're f____g jokin!

—*Oy, Selim! Dont keep hitting him—him not going to wake up.

—I will f__k yoo up.

—Hey Naseeb! Ho! You most be tell us, brudder. *Samjhe?* You my big brodder son, but eyu most be tell us. I cant protect eyu ennit.

They drag him up & his jerking lunges they spewed themselvs to berst.

How fast's his heart gooin? Baer engels hammer da walls. Ten thozand yeares between beats.

In the tidal surge th platelets pile.

His lif rushes by as rolling gobs of phagocyte...

—Wacche it! Wacch it! Bruv, hes going! S__t man, his checkin out!

—*Banc__d*, try it! Yu int gooin anyware. Don't even think abat it.

—Wache it! His puking it!

—*Let him do it!* Moderf__k, hes big hedache dis wan. Him nothing but hedache!

—*Kutti sallaa*, I will f__k yorr fammly up!

—*Selim, you dont leave it dead body here!*

They hawl him down & hammer dat bodi. An da jerking lungs are spewing da bathwater.

Yr man hes seeing ower shadders, owr shadowes crowding da lihte & hammering on da bodi.

Blood cells, macrophage, deform into signs.

> ... *A mattress in a takeaway... a girl amputated*
> *his mother punched*
> *a fat racist charity shop—*
> *looks back on three legs...*

Yeor man he saw us in his eyes as blue lihtg sprites, & we

spiral da capillariys of his eyeball.

A window opening in his heed.

And da platelets cram da places of hurt.

Yor creture feels his floting on rufgh hands. And sumwhare he heares banging feet on stars.

And da goons they lug him down the craeking stars, feeling lic hes floting aloong the seeling, an falling falling & never landing

shearing the atoms off a fals dawn, & falling falling on dusty planes

thinking he's in the border village on the white dirt road.

A caravanette with the side open and Selim with his fingers missing and a couple of boys.

And Ghulam and Raks hauling on a goat: *Load him in the back innit.*

Left his bones to bleach somewhere.

8 | *The Account of the Angel of the Left Hand*

In which Your creature is transported; and they seek help for Your creature; and the Angels and Soul and Judgement are suspended; and they return to Jannah.

§

(Fajr kadhib: 0354 GMT)

How long before the true dawn? Before we fly unto the Paradise of his heart, and the *Ruh* asking *How did ye leave the creature?*

And I will say... what do I say? Between this world and that for a thousand years shall he lie in the boot of a Sierra.

So our world is compacted in a mote. Whereof compared to Jannah even the middle of stars is barely embers. And within are all the angels ever created.

All the angels created within the chambers of the heart, they hammer the walls with *Huu!*

Would I were one of these—melting in the throngs of the thronging house, a sun one handsbreadth from my brow! Crying out to die, unable to bear my own love!

For my powers are spent to trace the Pen.

Say, the believers hurry hurry to their last *rooza*, while Your man has necked down a bath tub for *Suhoor*.

There is my wretch, between worlds in a car boot reeking of curries.

Sometimes I look on these fools and know as much about their world as a cod knows the forest fire.

And what can describe the space between boot and leaden sky? Verily, a false dawn that bleeds unto heaven. And a bag of bones a-rocking in the boot.

Truly his soul it floats on benzene fumes.

(Some angels imagine this soul so well it assumes a shape. But this shape has no top or bottom, nor colour or roughness, nor weight. Nathless, those images assume a shape.)

Truly his soul suspended in sleep. Then two shadows get out of the car, and go to the boot, in the false dawn.

Quick, say those shadows, *let's dump this spaz.*

But those villains are suspended for a thousand years in his sleep...

Before they haul him out and dump the wretch in the grounds of the hospital.

Before we make the *mi'raj*, and the *Ruh* shall say: *How did you leave His slave?*

Verily rasping in the bushes a thousand years. And the Noble Atid has stayed his Pen. And the Protectors have wrapped thin chill around.

And those Protectors: *Ya kiraman katibeen! Can ye stay his fate a jot? Man your bag of bones, O Followers! Hay! Hay! Hay! Hay!*

And what can describe a Preserved Tablet?

It is a canopy of ash trees in hospital grounds dripping *rahmat* on a shape.

A manky cat a-gasping in the bushes.

A sack race.

When he pushed a bully's face in snow.

And in his prostration he's trying to speak, but they've broken his jaw. He wants to say he's added a new spice to the curry pot. And sacrificed the Game. But they've broken his jaw.

There is a *hadith* that says at each good deed the Book is closed and the Angel ascends, and each good deed creates a new Angel. So the universe multiplies universe and is endlessly good.

And what if he were a devil and his entries so black? If you look but close enough you will see the Preserved Tablet itself is dancing and fluctuating—these *ayat* waiting for a hand to form. And the boat follows the waves.

Concussion buoys him on oceans.

We shear the atoms off a false dawn, & fall on dusty planes.

He sits by the road, tempting a goat with wild flowers. And derelict foundations of the hospital site and shredded tarp and mouldering construction signs. Three outcasts made a camp to smoke opium. The plain runs away to a distant village. Poppies dot the ditch.

   —**Eat, boy. Why don't you eat?*

Though the sun lie heavy on his limbs, his face swollen numb, he'd like to walk the bright dusty road, if the basking sun would lift...

   I haven't said goodbye. It's not too late. Not too late... *walking bright dusty road—*

And he's sitting in a long tin-roofed workshop with gawking children in vests and half-shirts, getting his mouth fixed. And Abba joins him with Arif in the A&E.

   And for some reason the boy's eyes tear up and body shakes. And Abba ruffles him:

   —*What you doing boy? You pain? You paining? Then why you* hoo hoo hoo? *You man now, innit. Yeah, my big man.*

His eyes tear up and Abba ruffles his hair.

—Hooowww hooww oww! Aha-ha-ha. Nooo no... You should make it other one cry, innit?

And his Abba ruffles his hair and gently shakes his neck.

And Arif turns embarrassed.

—You shame? Naa na. Hey stupid! You want me find them and put bullet in their leg?

The nurse came in with an injection.

—You want it? You want?

The nurse thought he was soft in the head:

—He needs it before I put stitches in, she says.

—Not need it! No. Not nee-eed. You want it boy? You think you can without dis? You show her what Pathan can do?

His swollen face an ache of love.

And then the children pile out of the workshop with a football, past the street metal beaters and cycle repairers, and he runs after the amputee bounding with a ball; the children surge like fish shoal.

And he sees a caravanette disappear into the honking traffic with put-puts and goats. And anguish grips him that Mom is sitting in the camper.

And if Mom is in the camper then Abba is there too.

And if they are there then he is too.

And then above the mouldering offices and tangled cables

and signs, one of the cars in distant traffic rises silently in a slow dive with a flash and dazzling dust.

Then a pearl bubbles from the trumpet of Israfil of the Soor to convulse the worlds.

And the cords strung between the Angels and their souls, those cords like an endless harp, these cords they sound the measure.

And we fly unto the Paradise of his heart. Whereof the middle of stars is barely embers. And within are all the angels ever created. And all those angels are but one Angel.

& the *Ruh* asks *How did ye find His creature?*

(And what if he were a devil and his entries ever so black?)

And I say: *I found him as I found them all. Ne can I trace namore the Eternal Light of Wisdom.*

(Fajr: 0554 GMT)

Part Two

Barzakh

1

An endless salt desert. And a shimmy of distant mountains. A buzz of flies around the bones.

Close your eyes and it could be the braying of reed pipes.

Open your eyes and there the flash of a tiny vehicle with a trail of dust.

The bus will shake with a hundred patch jobs, but the leathery driver will not let it die.

He twiddles the radio as he drives. Snatches of *ghazal*. Between the roar of the engine and the scrap of music on the edge of a crashing wavelength, the travellers seem utterly lost.

In their reveries they hear the unspoiled song, see the gestures of the singer.

There is the man, his light beard flecked with grey, his face almost younger. He holds onto a rattling seat, staring out, then at his fellow passengers.

Can you see them?

They stare back—a hard-looking man with a clump of black hair and eyes of Genghis; a worn couple with boxes of vegetables and a chicken; a woman in headscarf and her boy chaperone in a windcheater.

Only the young woman in burka behind him with a fat-faced baby avoids his glance.

See the sagging wires and snarled-up poles dipping to the distance; there a clutch of low buildings and vehicles breach the desert.

Wind rips through the bus, the music and static ebb and flow. And the man, he snaps his head back to glare at them. And the baby stares back.

And he grips his backpack.

The mountains fickle mauve.

Here is a ragtag checkpoint, where the trucks and buses stalled.

And an endless chain fence to denote the limits.

And the crowds who line up at the trestle tables or squat in the shade of buses with their permits.

Everything the colour of lime.

The border guards with boyish beards trawl the queues looking for something to confiscate, pretend to check documents.

Here is the man clutching his backpack, squeezing past to

the driver.

Say, *Where is this?*

And the driver babbling back.

Say, *Where is this? Where is here?*

Barzakh, Barzakh, says the driver.

And where is Barzakh? But the man must get off.

The young woman in burka joins the throngs clutching their papers.

And the man must follow, with the locals and battered workclothes and wicker baskets.

And the guards signal to wait their turn.

I have seen it before.

In there, the checkpoint booth, someone tries to tune a radio.

Listen, another *ghazal* is lost in hiss.

On the other side of the fence the sweating Chief sits with his officers and the tea seller. Over there the wiry man drags his box of contraband cigarettes from the battered bag in his car. And two officers, unimpressed with his offer, pick through the bag.

Now the woman in burka is called forth where the guards glance at her papers, sneak a look at her face, though she tries to veil her mouth. See how she holds a thin veil to her mouth, her baby under her chador, and stares at the ground.

The young guards bluff she can be detained and worse if she doesn't show her face.

That man wants to say something but grips his bag tighter—the Chief is confiscating banknotes from the smuggler's moneybag with a public show of duty.

And now the guards see the man in his kurta and leather jacket; they amble closer.

He looks to his neighbours:

—We need passport? Money?

But their faces are dumb. The guards stand close with their rifles cocked, mutter disdainfully.

—My papers?

And a villager who stares makes money signs with his fingers, and the man takes out paper notes, and the villager shows him—not this one, this one.

Now see there the toothless woman being checked alongside the woman in burka. She is angered by the guards' shamelessness, berates them loudly, in the way the toothless are bold. And now the man is startled by those shouting beside him.

And the soldiers are startled, they move to bully into silence but the crowd begins to heckle.

They bark at the crowd to make a second line, pull some for spot checks.

And the custom guards wake up, pull bags apart and spill them onto a table, then move to the next.

Listen to the woman in burka being reprimanded, ordered to take her veil down, while they scrutinize her papers. They will make her pay if they can.

The young guard with goggles signals the man.

He is motionless, the bag is beating to his heart.

The soldier frowns—beckons him sharply.

And the man tries to shuffle forward.

And now, say—can you see beyond the fence! And that man he stops, his eyes strain in the glare.

And the guard pulls down his goggles and turns to stare.

And sudden shouts from soldiers on the far side! Hoarse and panicked!

That young guard's arm outstretched to keep them back, twisting to see what's happening over there. Can you see!

And he turns to see the man break out in sweat, his eyes awry, slipping through uneasy crowds.

Halt, he shouts. But there are soldiers running beyond the fence.

And the fat captain sweeping his arm this way and that. *Halt*, he shouts. And the man is moving into the trampled plain.

—*There's another one here! There's another one!*

And two shots crack beyond the fence, and the crowds break like a flood. The guard pushing through them after the man, who throws his bag away, and the guard shoots in the air. And an explosion rips across the desert, and the man falls to ground until voices bellow over his head and a rifle butt smashes his head.

2

I know this journey.

Sightless. In a jawbreaking truck.

A boot... grinding my head. A blindfold cutting the sockets.

I knew this fear.

I dreamt I never wanted the roar of the truck to stop.

Did I dream it stopped? And gross hands haul me up and a moment suspended in air and I don't know when the ground will hit...

... and coming round to a frog march with hands cuffed behind; and my head pounding, and barking voices like they've slipped into the radio.

Did I come round?

Doors clang open and I'm dragged from afternoon heat into cool. I'm spinning in darkness, but surely I saw the shapes in the doorway... before it shut. Are those hands around my shoulders?

I'm spinning into darkness. A corridor. A corridor in my head? And metal screeching behind walls.

I must be senseless. For it's black, with shambling guards and talons in my shoulders, my hands in stocks behind my back, and these beasts snuffling and grunting—they haul me like rubbish...

Listen—bolts or an iron gate snap open, and a furnace heat jumps out to buffet. A person groaning in a dream, wrapped in a canvas, raised in the air, going headfirst...

They hauled me like a rubbish bag going into a column of heat, a blaze that lights up the blindfold. Even the smell of smoke in the dream.

And I too jerked in their grip, with my hair crackling and head shrivelling, and screaming like him.

3

I think I'm awake—my trainers dragging on dirt and broken tiles, as I'm hauled by lumbering beasts, head clamped down, noises growling in the walls.

Listen—a rusting bolt, the crack of door frame. And ratcheting wheels and chains. What is this medieval freakshow?

I try talking through bloody gums. My head on fire. And I'm crammed into some closet reeking of wood... pulleys creaking, to squeeze me.

I hear a slat shut, and my breath crowding my ears. And I'm spinning in darkness. Darkness that may not be night. And dreams less confused.

He was strapped on the high hospital bed. Across the ward patients sat or tottered with doleful visitors. He was aware he had no one and that his patient's gown might have ridden up to expose his privates.

Doctors came to shine a light in his eyes and feel his face. He felt he must be swollen for their hands hovered above the skin. He said Yes whenever they asked if it hurt though he couldn't feel a thing.

Can you remember any more today?

And the consultants seemed delighted if he couldn't.

There was a reassuring posh voice:

It's quite common with this kind of insult to the head. You may find all the other pieces fall into place and you have these odd pockets of memory loss.

How long am I out?

In my dream I still have teeth, licking a swollen mouth for water. My head one throb that's bled into the reeking wood.

I'm standing in a coffin. And my ankle is dead. And the other one crawling.

Listen—that wailing coming close—

I hear the cell open next to mine—the wheels strain, and crack, squeezing my heart.

Someone babbling in another tongue as he's pushed in.

Then wailing as his box winches, wailing, Aiiee! Aiiee!

A door clangs and the goons slouch away.

I can see nothing.

Do we all whine like this? Talk as if someone listens? Whispering rubbish, apologizing. Shouting, whispering.

—*Waylun yawma-ithin lilmukaththibeen...*

It's like I know what he's saying. Like I see his hatchet face laughing to himself, biting his lip like a fool.

And I'm awake in the madhouse. I know what he's saying—I can say it too…

—*Alam nashrah laka sadrak, Wawadaa'na anka wizrak, Allathee anqada thahrak…*

My ankle is crawling. Something crawling.

I'm holding my breath. I must be hallucinating it's crawling up my knee. If I could see down there.

—*Fa inna ma'al usri yusraa, Inna ma'al usri yusraa.*

I'm hallucinating a black glitter under a thread of light, creeping along my thin *kurta*. But I don't want to give myself away.

Banchod, I see a plated black tail arcing up.

—There's something on me!

That next man has stopped now. I can see his bug eyes popping out of his head. And just my breathing.

—Someone! Can you hear me?

I must be hallucinating it's crawling on my neck.

—There's something on me! Get it off!

Any moment I will feel its sting.

Then a shutter snaps back with a shaft of light. And I see a crescent black tip of a tail under my chin. And a needle, a stiletto pokes through the slot, to skewer something twisting on my neck, its tail striking the spike. And the stiletto's gone through my neck in the hollow above my collarbone—I can barely groan through the grimace... and the spike skewers straight through my shoulder into the wood behind—and I'm grunting like a pig, and it's twisting on my skin.

And thank God the blackness comes...

4

I'm dreaming I saw something in the shutter, before the spike goes back, with the wriggling thing on it.

I can hear me whimpering in the dream, and thinking *What was that?* Red eyes in a mask, or red lights, maybe a helmet, maybe military headgear.

And I'm dreaming someone whispers to me like a wittering fool, until I wake up wedged inside a cupboard, and someone is whispering:

—Assalaamualaykum, brother.

And my heart is hammering the cage.

—Hello, Englishman.

Everything amplified. He can hear me try to straighten up, with my dead leg.

—Assalaamalaykum, brother. What is your name? I speak English. I am Syeed Muhtadi. Brother, you are also here?

I'm not biting, and he sighs.

—Wallaahi, you are here. Why we are here? Ach, yes. Only tell me. These hypocrites what they say I have done? Where is the proof? Yes, who they are? Everybody I treat like my own. Wallaahi!

May Allah reward these! Muhtadi's word is to the misguided, but Allah misguide them!

He's rasping like he hasn't drunk. And I'm suddenly parched.

—*wanahshuruhum yawma alqiyamati aala wujoohihim aaumyan wabukman... wasumman... mawahum jahannamu kullama khabat zidnahum saaeeran...* Shaytan test the friends of Allah. They think they deceive Allah, the hypocrites, but they shall be deceive.

His rasp vibrating in my coffin.

—*Hatha yawmu la yantiqoon, wala yuthanu lahum faya aatathiroon.* They say me, *Why do they say this?* Should I be them unjust? Should I not guide them? But Allah is guide... I only say to protect them. Let them say false! I forgive them! They are young. But *Allah taala* not forgive those who attack the *wali*—*Waylun yawma-ithin lilmukaththibeen!*

We strain in the silence.

—They lie with Shaytan!

And my heart is hammering the cage.

—How I am guilty for what their hand did? I am their friend. Not even friend. They know me. That is my weakness. I am friend to all. *Khalas.*

—Shut up, man!

—Ach, friend, ach, ach. You are here also.

His voice is a whisper.

—But inshallah we can help each other. I can help. You tell me. I can help inshallah.

I strain to the whisper.

—Think, friend. What they say you. What it could be. Hah? Muhtadi he can help. Believe me, you not punish. But you speak to Muhtadi all. Hello? Hello, Englishman.

I'm not biting, and he sighs.

—You are afraid. You fear punish. But fear Allah. You will let unjustice happen? You will not. Brother, you are Muslim? I know you are Muslim. You are Muslim? You are friend to Muslim? Then how you can let one Muslim brothers suffer by *kaafiroon*? We are one *ummah*. If one Muslim brother suffer unjustice we must make the efforts.

I'm straining to hear past the blood in my ears.

—We must be help each other. You tell me. I help you. You tell them you know those who say to me bad things. Tell them—they lie. I tell them—you are good man—

—Go to Hell!

I deafen myself.

And how long do we listen? With head on fire and ears stuffed with silence?

—This is my mistake. Muhtadi will trust. It is my *zaat*. I think for their suffering. If I see brother-sister suffering torture and bad thing, from them I can turn my face? I cannot. Now my fate I am sold by those devils. But Allah sees. May they be punish—*wathooqoo aa'athaba alhareeqi—Thalika bima qaddamat aydeekum waanna Allaha laysa bithallamin lilaa abeedi!*

And when I hear the crack of winching pulleys my heart jerks it's my coffin walls—

but it's his cell—his shrieking, his wood and ropes or whatever grinding: that fool shrieking like a pig till his knackers are crushed…

and I'm listening to grunting wood and things snapping—

and then pulleys ratchet snap, and I know it's my turn: my shoulders to buckle, my head to crack till snot bubbles pop, and I don't know what I'm grunting when I go spinning out…

5

Three female consultants with soft voices sat him in front of an imaging machine and shone a probe into his ear.

On the screen the camera eased through the whorls of his brain while the one with scented hands said:

What do you think of that whitening at the edges of the larynx?

Another said, It does look like reflux.

A long time ago I wet myself.

My lips split open. My eyes must be ballooned up.

But I don't know if I'm awake.

I dreamed they took me out and put me into the furnace again—they threw me headfirst into white-hot fire and I never touched the sides. And my skin... must have... and they brought me back.

Or they did take me... and I can't remember, I don't want to remember.

A tap on the shoulder.

Soft drumming on the frame of this box. Does light ghost in?

Then it pings my ear, my head. It knocks on my eye but I don't feel it. And I realise I'm blindfolded.

I try to straighten but my ankle throbs. I crane my face to the trickle. It tastes like water.

It rains down and I drink and let it wash my hair. I let it collect in my mouth and neck it down. And too late it turns to something fetid. And I jam my head down and retch it out.

I rip my throat and scream.

—What do you want! What do you want!

But my mouth is swelled up.

And the trickle comes to a stop. And I have an angry cry.

After a while I can feel a brush of air—where the shutter must be. Something breathing there. Watching me cry.

Keep your shoulders high, don't let them take your heart. My mouth is banged up but I mumble:

—I'm British. You understand? British. I want to speak to someone.

Who is there? Is it a gorilla? Am I talking to the boiler?

—They're going to hear about this.

Then my innards contract when pulleys clatter and the cell squeezes tight.

I'm going, *Hey! Hey! Stop! Why are you doing this! You can't do this, man! I've done nothing!*

It holds me in a vice. But I am not mangled.

—Please. I don't—I don't know what I've done. I'm just—I've never even been here... I was just at the border stop, and—you can't hold me! What for? I don't know what's going on.

There is a light come brighter under the blindfold, I can feel heat. They could fry my eyeball but I bluff it:

—I'm being held illegal... you can't blindfold me! I'm just a traveller, trying to get home!

A gleam of orange metal under the blindfold, and it's gone—and then I bang my head against the wood when it touches my brow. There's a smell of burning hair as it sears my head. I'm going *Heeeyy!*

And something rumbling—machinery, voices, I don't know.

—What do you want? I don't know what I've done!

Then the walls crank apart, and my knees don't work, and I collapse on the spot.

It feels like gross hands haul me like rubbish, dragging along a passage with cries from other walls...

When he looked down he saw he had a perfect right leg from the knee.

It felt like his own calf and veins and hair but he was told it was a prosthetic.

The physiotherapist insisted his middle ear needed to relearn balance, and wedged him between parallel bars. But he strolls up and down disdainfully. And his physio took him for a longer walk through the corridors,

and a bolt door is unlocked and he's thrown head-first...

Did I hear a buzz of flies when my face hit the floor?

I went out in darkness and wake up in darkness.

It's quiet now. I don't think I've been out long. But my face scraped raw. I panic I'm blinded. But it feels airier. Then a stench of shite.

I say, *Hey*, just for myself. And try to get upright, but my hands are shackled behind, my head can't work out up or down. And for an age I'm hurting and shaking. And then I find a rough wall standing in debris and I shuffle along with my shoulder. Away from the smell. Until I'm hurting too much and lie down and pray for sleep.

6

Let him sleep. This is the kindest deed I can give him.

What other deeds have my hands laid up? I cannot remember.

Astaughfirullah Alazeem, Astaughfirullah Alazeem...

There he is—a young man like the others. He is stirring. Does he struggle to sleep or to wake up?

He is moaning... Sleep. Sleep.

Let me make *salat*. With my chains. With my worn-out sandals. With no water. With a broken crumbling wall for *mihrab*.

The engines are screeching in unseen chambers.

Why am I praying?

As many times I prostrated I have not prostrated. Circling the Kaaba I have not circled the Kaaba. I meditate my sins yet I cannot find my sins...

Light leaks into the broken roof, through the chinks in the stone, filling the space with gloomy paleness.

A pall of despondence came on me in some unknown past. Since then each day is unique in its futility.

Do you see? He is stirring.

Sleep. Sleep.

He is groaning, trying to get up. Rocking against the wall. Sliding along the wall. Do you see? He finds a chink in the rotting wall—air! Can he feel warm light? the flies stirring?

Then let me go to him.

Ah, but I see him struggling with his bound hands—twisting them from round his back—to undo his trousers, and work his underwear down. And he puts his head against the wall and feet back from the fallen rubble. And the smell of his urine fills this lofty hold.

It trickles to a stop, and I hear him breathing, *Oh Jesus*.

—*Ghufraanak.*

And now he doesn't breathe. And he slowly pulls up his trousers.

—Who's that?

Who? What can I say to him? I cannot say if I am this man or that. I cannot tell if I have been here a thousand years. Did I ever live? For the dream of my life has even evaporated.

—What do you want! Hello? Do you speak English? You got no rights over me. I've done nothing. You can't hold me.

He cannot speak properly. But I understand. Let me breathe my *zikr*...

—What do you want me to say! I don't know anything!

Astaughfirullah Alazeem. What can I say to him?

—You are blameless?

He is surprised.

—On my mother's life, I've done nothing. Ask me anything.

I have done nothing! Truly, I am one who is cursed by seventy thousand days of torpor.

And then I hear him say:

—For ffffucksake.

He is listening to the noises—the ratchet of engines, the inhuman grunts beyond these high walls.

His leg won't hold and he is shaking.

—Well? What you waiting for? You think I'm guilty? Do it! Go on. If you're gonna do it—do it! But you—you—you're gonna pay.

He is listening to the sounds beyond this high keep. Like the squealing of saws and shaking metal sheets. And I sit back down with my chains.

Astaughfirullah alazeem, astaughfirullah alazeem...

—Who are you then? Are you with them? Are you a prisoner? Talk to me then! Why are you here?

—I am like you.

—I'm blindfolded. You understand blindfolded? I can't see. Can you help me?

Can I help? As many times I helped someone I helped myself.

—*Banchod,* can you help! Can you see?

—I see.

—Well can you help me?

He edges towards my voice, and his knee catches my shoulder, and he crouches down.

—Please, help me.

My hands seem to reach across a vast distance, before they take off his blindfold.

He nearly blacks out, and he can open one flooding eye.

Let me see through his eye: here is light seeping through holes in a high, broken roof. Onto a crumbling, pockmarked wall where most of the render has fallen to the floor. Onto a shape, an old man in a dirty kurta and the stuffing come out of his jacket. And my leg iron fixed to the wall.

—Why are you here, Baba?

—It was Allah's Will.

—Allah's Will! Allah's Will! I think some pigs with machine guns had a hand!

Then a worn out screaming starts beyond the wall.

He is dragging his leg around, his hands shackled, to find cracks where he can squint with his good eye and see scrub and emptiness.

—What are you doing, old man? Waiting for your turn?

He limps around the long hold, the rubble piled to the corners, past the heap of rags with a mass of flies dancing, and comes to the middle to look up.

Now he sees the outer wall in the raking light. The mortar gouged and fallen, and the hooks and spikes sticking out at intervals. Do you see the graffitied lines worked and overlaid, hand after hand in the surface? Layer after layer of Arabic and other signs. They scrawl from the dirt floor to the top of broken render as a wrinkled grey sea. A pitted cuneiform tablet. Young men like him, old men like me, marking our signs... for what?

And a creature in another keep is shrilling.

—What's that then? They coming round with birthday cake? Yeah, you sit on your arse and pray Allah-Allah. You deserve what's coming to you.

—May Allah finish with me.

—I wish he'd finish you an' all! Oh, come on, man! Come on! He's not finished with *me*! Help us!

Shaytan tells me to sit trembling in delight of Your punishment. Why should I seek to escape my judgement? I run faster to the Fire.

Some creature is shrilling.

And I get up.

And I look up, pointing past the ridge of render, where the wall breaks to a decrepit window slit. And I tap my shoulder.

—What? Up there? Up there! Climb on you? Did you notice I've got my hands cuffed behind? Why don't *you* go up?

I reach to feel his leg irons. Then tap my own crusted iron, and a gap where the manacles hold with a thick screw. I see his exasperation, and I pick up a broken hook from the floor, and mimic forcing the gap with the straight heel of the hook. I turn him around and steady my shaking hand to work the manacle.

—Did you ever think about trying it on yourself?

Myself? I have not a drop of mercy to accompany me. But perhaps his fate can be different.

This hurts him, but he hears the agony behind other walls.

—Just do it!

What if I break his wrists? What can he do then? But I am a physician who must ignore the patient's groans. And before his wrists break the bands prise apart enough to slip his hands.

He curls up moaning and tending his wrists.

—You are one strong *Dada*.

He looks again at the window but cannot see a way to it. He takes the hook and looks for clefts in the stones of the outer wall. He worries at mortar that falls away as he breathes on it. But the ragged stone yields more slowly. He looks for soft spots, digs here, moves on. While someone cries in pain.

Not here, he says. He must find a corner, out of the way. He works frantically, like an animal—dig, dig. Till his fingers cramp. Dig. Dig.

—Don't mind me, Khan sahib. You have a lie down. You mullah types—you make me laugh.

Till his fingers cramp. And he sits panting.

—Don't wear your trousers past your ankles, say a *du'a* when you fart…You got a *du'a* for digging yourself out?

And a massive blow shakes the earth. And mortar and dust showers down from the walls. And the screaming has stopped.

What engine of death was this?

And the man scrambles up to look at the wall. See the waves of lines, the signs hewn in the stone, the marks scratched over the signs, that scrawl endlessly across the gouged-out pages of a book as thick as a cliff. He sees crumbling footholds. That reach

to that big hook. And the distant broken cleft of a window.
He beckons me to the wall and taps his shoulder.

—*Dada*, it's time to go. Me up. On your back. That's
right.

La hawla wa la quwwata illa billah.

We are the same stature. And I brace against the wall, and
he clambers on to my knees and shoulders onto the wall. And
whatever pain is in his limbs is forgotten.

—*La hawla wa la quwwata illa billah.*

Say, had I not also made this ascent? My fingers cut on
mouldering marks, that crumble into other signs. And kicked a
toehold in a cliff that dissolves as I climb. He too jumps to reach
that big hook, but this wall is made of ash, and breaks under his
feet as he scrabbles, but he clings to the hook!—one hand, two
hands—and it loosens in this shifting house of sand. He presses
his feet against the wall and walks up to his hands, his body coiled,
and if he could climb on the hook...

And then the stonework gives way and the hook flies out
and he is falling over my head.

He cannot breathe, cannot move.

I put a hand on his head and bring his knees to his chest.
And when he can breathe and moan he rolls into a ball and
nothing is broken.

Unreal voices bark in another cell.

The big hook is in his hand—a hole where it tore away mortar and stone.

From the floor we can both see a mousehole of light where he ravaged the corner. But now he has the hook with long pointed ferrule.

He crawls to the corner and breathes in a flicker of wind. He scrapes away the rubble and strikes at the crevice and nearly falls through: the corner cracks like honeycomb.

There is a massive blow in the other cell—shuddering through my knees and belly.

And he thrusts at the corner and the stone disintegrates, yellowing, mouldering, until he has a hole. And there is a dazzling glimpse of desert.

—Where are we? Do you know where the border is?

—*La hawla wa la quwwata illa billah.*

—Jesus Christ.

He rams at the hole with flakes flying, and tries his head, then rams more.

He pushes his head through the foxhole, and I cannot hear him.

I hear the other man and the sound of chains.

And I close my eyes. And I see him on a rack, and the grinding of a winch and a mouth grimacing, the winch ratcheting back a mace the size of a man.

—Do you know where we are? Mister!

And he drags me, drags the old fool to the foxhole, and forces my head through the hole.

And I am blinded in another world.

Out here the cries are faint.

The sun caresses my face.

I know he is shouting to me.

And when I can open my eyes I see an old army truck, and oil drums and plastic cans, and the ground sloping away, with the ground dropping off like a table. And a shimmer of distant mountains. And bird cry.

Ya Allah, what are You trying to show me? The more knowledge You gave me, the more I shrank from the world.

And then he drags me back in.

—Do you know where we are? Do you know where we are!

—I know.

And there's a blow that shakes the ground through to my stomach and the wall rains down. Then cranking of wheels and chains again.

—How far's the border? Do you know the way?

And we hear another door clang.

I hear the devil dogs, the belching Hell.

Let it be over.

And he fixes the hook in my shackle and it peels off like a toy.

—You git. You useless... You could have...

And the man rakes and kicks at the hole and tries to get his shoulders through, and at the far end I hear the lock of the door. And he struggles half-through, he struggles half-through.

I hear the lock and the bolts at the far end.

His feet kick through and disappear, and I am alone.

The door crashes open and I turn my head aside from the punishers. They stand at the door. And I feel the ground shake as they stride.

And the man reaches through the hole and grips my beard and hauls my head out. And I feel the ground shaking as they stride across the long hold. And he drags my shoulders, legs, out!—drags me to my feet. And we hobble to an old army truck, standing outside the ancient fort, with the ground dropping off to endless scrub desert.

—Do you know how to hotwire this?

He jumps into the truck looking for guards. And looks

down at the wheel:

—Yes Allah! Yes Allah! *Jazaakallah! Jazaakallah! Jazaaaakallah khair!*

He turns the key, he turns the key in the ignition and it shakes into life.

—Yes Allaaaaah! Get in, man! Get in! Where are the bastard guards?

And he gets the truck moving down the track.

—Which way the border!

I am looking back at the fort and a door opens and I see them. Two of them. Watching. Unhurried.

And I turn my head and close my eyes in dread. And he checks in the wing mirrors.

—Do you see them? What are they doing?

He hammers the truck down a track off the plateau, down a rutted track past curving banks of crab trees. And he cranes his head to see the mouldering fort.

And he starts banging the wheel—harder and harder:

—We've got their truck. This is the only truck! Yaah! Yaa-ah! Fuck you! Yaa-aaaah! Come on, old man! *Hamdulillah!*

And then he starts crying.

—Fuck you.

The cabin has loose cigarettes in the gearbox, and rocks of sugar, and a water flask that we drain, and a plastic bottle of some Cola that has boiled here for how long.

The man keeps searching for a lighter or matches. He keeps looking for pursuers.

The man keeps asking *Where is the border?*

He keeps looking at the cracked face of his watch. It doesn't work but he keeps looking. He keeps looking for helicopters.

The truck hammers the parched steppes towards the blue smudge on the horizon.

He fiddles with the radio transmitter, each channel crackling static.

—They must be radioing ahead. What do I do if we get something? Hey? You gonna tell me what they're saying? Are you any good with this? Jump in any time, *chattu*.

Behind is the distant table rising like a blister on the plain with the square scab of the fort.

I remember those shapes.

—They must have put out an alert. We need the Embassy, uncle. You understand? British Embassy. Hello?

I'm looking at this man's battered face, the burn on his forehead, his hand that aches on the gearbox, his wrong foot that presses the pedal. I feel it all.

—You've got Alzheimer's, haven't you? Alzheimer's? We—need—British—Embassy.

—This is Barzakh.

The man is staring with his good eye.

—What do you mean, *This is Barzakh*? You saying there's no Embassy? There's a British Embassy in every pisspot on the planet. You can probably find one in Hell.

—No.

The man squints for an answer.

—All right—which way then, Baba? Hah? Across the mountain? Where's the border? Hello? Border?

—All is border.

—Awwgh. A straight answer! Please. Where do I go? That way? The other side?

The blood caked around his face, his eye swelled up, his good eye staring.

—Is that where I'm going? Other side?

Was I waiting for him? Or was he waiting for me?

And I nod.

—Thank you, God.

Here are the flurries of vegetation and ruinous homes and goats in the scrub. And here the locals lift their heads from planting or turn their back by the roadside.

The road picks up a river bed with a runnel of water. And we have a water flask. But who knows how much time?

—You know, you could have escaped any time. What, were you too mashed? Too scared?

Escape?

—I mean it's better than hanging around for... What were you waiting for?

What was I waiting for?

—How long were you banged up? Do you even know? Did you do something? Grow your beard too long? Is that a *No?* Coz I gotta tell you, I ain't got a clue why they jacked me.

What do I remember?

—Were you like me?

—Like you.

—I tell you blatant, I can't remember crap. I think they kicked my brains out.

The lorry hammers a green plain. The man looking for a sign of other vehicles. But there are only motorbikes loaded with green melons, and limping pickups and carts.

And he carries on pushing buttons for the radio transmitter. And bursts of harsh voices in the silence. And every time he looks to me, *Uncle, what was that?*

And the truck hammers for how long?

What dream is this? I'm dreaming of a truck roaring in my ears, and wind on my face, and radio static. Of green plains, and wild animals in the distance, and tiny villages with orchards and goat flocks. I cannot remember ever sleeping. But now I fall into exhaustion...

Did I sleep?

Or did I watch the mountain nearing imperceptibly, rising sheer? And the river bed falling below.

And I wake when he stops the lorry and keeps it running, and for a moment he hangs transfixed from the cab as he sees his face in the wing mirror—sees a grotesque stranger—before he clambers down the bank to the strip of alluvial stream.

I climb out of the cabin and see him put his cracked lips to the stream, just a few fingers deep. And there he struggles out of his trousers and sits in the stream and washes himself, his trousers and his hair.

There is a path down the bank to squat stones. This water glittering hard in stony bed. By the ten million insects that hover on its surface. Here I can make my *wudhu* for the first time.

Here is *Jannah*. But the thought is bitter.

That man fills the flask, he climbs a little up the bank to fasten his trousers. Hurrying hurrying. Then starts back for the road. But I am at the water's edge standing in *salat*.

—There's no time for that shit anymore!

And there is the sound of a vehicle hammering from afar. And I hear the man scrambling up the bank:

—Dada! Dada! We gotta breeze!

And I hear a vehicle hammer until it thunders in my head. I hear a voice say, *I'm gone!*

But I make my *salat*. Oh Allah, help me to remember you. May You forgive us our heedlessness.

I hear a voice say, *You maderchod!*

He is waiting at the truck. With tears of fury.

—*Maderchod... maderchod!*

The lorry is thrashed to the foot of the mountain.

He says, *This way? Up there?* But he does not wait for an answer.

The lorry is thrashed to the foot of the mountain.

Here is this boy, so eager to live. Even to save me. He wishes us to run to our fate. Those with shining faces hurry anxiously to their Lord. The guilty must wait. Those with froward brows are afraid.

He doesn't speak.

Listen—can you hear the awful blow! And the wailing like ten million insects.

—What is it? You hear something? Is it a copter? I think I hear it. I hear it! I'm not going back, *dada*. You get me? This is it. We dead meat now.

He doesn't speak.

He says, *My leg is killing me.*

The man is shaking his broken watch.

—This gauge says we still got some petrol. I thought you had an accent, uncle. Has it gone? Say something, uncle. What's your name? I'm Naseeb.

What is my name?

—Whassa story? Like me, you said. What, too much Charley? Women? Talk to me, uncle.

—Like you.

—Like me? You look like my granddad. You know that? I swear.

And then he says:

—I can't really remember him. Maybe I remember him coz of you.

We grind past a cart with a scrawny horse. And a last

flourish of trees before the sheer mountain rise, and the river dropping down.

The truck curves round with the river dropping down, it starts the winding climbs. Narrow or steep he keeps it growling at the same speed. But fear can no longer keep him awake. He nods.

Each time I look at him he is awake. Checking the petrol gauge.

Each time the bracelet of river drops further.

He keeps it growling at the same speed.

I wake with something singing in my ears. And we are passing something on the roadside: like two bruised pumpkins.

—What the ff—-!

That boy he whips his head and tries to see in the side mirror.

—Did you see that?

Did I see it? What shall my eyes answer on Judgement Day? What shall my hands answer? It is written on my skin. They shall peel and bubble from the bones to testify. Shall they judge against me?

—You saw that, right? You did. You must have.

He slows the truck to a shuddering stand.

—Should I stop? Uncle, you want me to stop?

Out of the side door—I see the roadside dotted in the distance with stones. And wailing on the wind: like voices drawn keening through a bottle mouth.

—What is it? It's an animal, right? What do you see?

They lie distant. But I see them. Those smashed heads shouldering out of the broken earth as obscene flowers, the rocks dotting the ground. Can you hear a music of flies? And those voices keening through a bottle mouth?

I shut the door.

—Was it a goat or something?

The boy starts the lorry rolling. He keeps looking to me:

—I'll stop if you want.

The lorry shuddering in low gear.

—There's probably a convoy after us. We better not stop.

That boy brooding at the wheel. He is afraid of his thoughts.

—I'm not stopping for anyone. *Samje?*

He worries about the petrol.

Nothing is said until the truck is rolling on fumes and he stops at a fork. In the sudden quiet there's a distant drone in my ear that makes me look to the horizon.

Ahead are specks of dwellings on the facing mountain. And a dirt road forks off around a shoulder.

And the boy jumps into the back of the lorry, and roots amongst crates and jerry cans. And opens one with a *Bismillah*. And smelling it it is petrol.

Up here the sun is still high.

Ahead are specks of dwellings on the facing mountain. The other way the dirt road disappears round the shoulder.

That boy broods.

—There's gotta be a checkpoint that way. We gotta go a back route. Uncle, what do you think?

He starts walking up the blind bend.

—You don't think we'd end up in the Gobi desert? Is it even heading in right direction? That's West, right? Can you tell by the sun? Don't be scared to chip in, *chattu*.

I make a long step from the cabin, and buckle to the knees on the road.

—We could get stranded.

He is imagining it must go to the border. The other road winding the ridge to the facing mountain, the villages, the spies.

—There's gotta be a roadblock or something. We gotta go backways. We can't be seen.

Have you seen a mountain in unreal light? And wind

across grasses? How has Allah eased our way?

When we climb the cabin again the man says, We need water, boss. And he drives for the facing mountain.

I cannot run away. I acknowledge the day. And have covered myself in forgetfulness before each iota of good and bad is made to speak.

And I pray *Fatiha*.

7

My head is fucked and the sun still high.

How did we get this far?

I keep hearing the tinkle of goats above the gears. There's goats perched a few feet above our heads gnawing at the wicker weave as we pass.

Every time I nod and wake up the truck is still rounding a bend.

That old man's face is constipated, fist and eyes shut.

The homesteads are set back with stony paths.

My hand can't grip the gearstick and my ankle is going to fall off.

See this track twisting into a terraced farm and outbuildings.

We need water, I say.

I let the truck in and get as much cover as there is. But it's a military truck.

The engine is killed. And in the still I hear a constant rumble from beyond the mountains like roadworks or construction in my ear. And turning my head this way, that way, it wipes away the sound for a moment before it swims back in.

That old man's fist and eyes are shut. Keeping out the world.

I say, *Maybe you should come too. Ask them where we're headed.*

I'm just about to switch when Rip Van Winkle opens his eyes and stirs.

He does it deliberately. He must do.

There's an empty cart, and the shell of a car. Tables outside the farmhouse all plaster and earthworks. The windows shuttered or black. Nothing stirs in the outhouses. Goats bleating a long way off.

And my man has got his dithery hands over his ears. He starts hobbling up a hill in the direction of maybe a low-walled shrine with a worn-out tree.

I call after him, *How do you say Water?*

I'd be well rid.

Now I'm circling the house with my empty flask. What would happen to them if they're caught helping us? I got no choice though, have I?

I say *Hello*, too quiet to be heard.

There's a battered shed with a squat-down toilet, a wall tap and metal jug. And I've got an overwhelming desire for a crap.

Closing that door and squatting in the dark it feels like back in the box.

What if the owners come? Or the goon squad?

I should hurry but nobody gets busted on the bogs—that's not in the game, is it? This is arley barley.

And for the first time I start praying. Let me finish my business before they find the lorry.

And when I turn the tap it coughs and gives nowt. Ain it. Turn it full and there's nuffink.

—O-oh God.

I can't move.

Fucksake Allah, you're not keeping your side of it. Finish me if you want. But why shit on me as well?

I peep out of the door. Is this how it ends? Shot by the pigs waddling around with my arse hanging out? I'd rather that than the family find me cock in hand. *Scuse me madam, could I trouble you for a glass of water?* Allaa-ah.

Did I see a water trough or bucket? I hold onto my trousers and the metal jug and shuffle round the back of the house. Still no one. And I spot a pump and I can wash myself, squeaking water, one eye on the windows.

I'm scared of that house. I can't knock on the door. I'd rather jack the stuff—water, food, blanket, torch, knife, money.

Best to keep them out of it.

But I'm scared of that house. Why? After everything that's happened.

Up in the window I swear there's a shape in the shadow, the top pane. It could be a face. The head would have to be near the ceiling, jutting forward. And I imagine the arms are bound behind a beam.

I'm climbing the hill, with a petrol can of water and an armful of apples. And I'm calling but he doesn't hear.

Go on dada, pray for all their souls. I bet he's got his eyes shut an all.

—Have you finished *namazing*? Coz why don't we do all the ones you've missed in jail?

Now I see the hawks circling the mount and on the tree the crows. There's a scattering of rubble and bits. And there's a hum.

I reach the brow and the little wall hides a cemetery of earth graves bounded by stones and with sprigs of broken branches.

And I'm thinking there's an unfinished burial... the earth flung up, the stones... there's shit got bruck up here. And I'm thinking *What's in the grave?*

Over there a tomb with wooden door and gate fence: it's been hammered.

Now I see—now I see five bodies around the shrine in

broken attitudes. The flies are wailing like reed pipes, but there is no smell. The faces have leathered, the eyes are gone. I can't see half their limbs. *Allahu Akbar.*

I stand by the old man and don't breathe.

I see nails and shrapnel in the faces, in the door of the tomb, in the stone wall.

The old man is praying *du'a* with his hands over his face. And his voice an animal wail.

I take him down the hill and help him into the truck.

The same blank folk move aside on the road. Do they know? Do they care?

My man is with the fairies—he's listening to his voices outside the truck—

—Wha is going on!

I can see the world flood back into his head.

—We should get word out about this place. People should do something!

Dad's Army is counting his prayer beads.

—*La hawla wa la quwwata...*

—You're not angry? You think we shouldn't be angry?

—*... wa illa billah*—

—That's God? That's not God! That's people! How they do that to their own? If it was me I'd—! And what are you doing, uncle? Counting your *tasbih*? Is that your answer? Chha, people like you, man. What were you put on this planet for?

I go to grab the *tasbih* but the bloke is suddenly tonk!

Another hump-backed peasant shuffles to the verge as we grind on.

—What is this place? What are they—? That ain't living. These people are dead!

But my man is listening out of the window again.

—Do you know where we are! I don't believe it. You tricked me, didn't you? Fff—Christsake... I'm never getting outta here.

—Inshaallah.

—You know, you talk too much.

I don't know what I'm doing here. I don't know how long I've been driving except my ankle is going to drop off.

And the road rides a switchback under the ridge until it goes slap into the mountain face and splits either way. And I see the square sign stuck in the limestone.

One look at Dad's Army and I reckon I'll check this out by myself. And I've got out and squinnying up at Russian words and weird ones in English.

I don't want to ask him, but I'm asking him:

—You heard of Das-gar...? Das-what? Yeah, Dasghar. What about Sej—? Sejli—Sejli-hee... What's that say? Is it saying miles? Do you know where we are? Aah, sha'up, geez.

I look at the big sign for time.

—Dasghar. Dar al Huu... Hu... wak—kal. Sej— something. How do you say that? Sejlihyat. Hey, uncle! Are any of these by the border?

The old man's come out and he's staring up at the signpost. It's like he doesn't see anything on it.

But I'm thinking to myself. There's a fuzzy hole in my head, little fragments, a perfume, a sneeze that won't come. But I'm feeling it, I'm getting vibes.

—Sejlihyat?

When I look at these names they start to link.

Have I been...? Please God. I have...

But how? When would I have...?

—I know it.

Holy...

You wouldn't cheat me Allah? Would You? You're guiding me, Man.

I know that name.

—Baba! Hey, Baba! How far's that say? Sejlihyat.

And the old man is looking at it again like he doesn't see the sign. And he's shaking his head. I'll probably find out he can't read. And he says:

—The book writes our name for no reason.

I'm looking at him like I'm gonna switch.

—That's really good. You should write poetry. So how far is Dasghar?

And he looks at me.

—Far.

—So how far's far? Twenty? Thirty? Miles?

My man he seems to weigh it up and nods.

—Yes.

—Twenty miles? Twenty feet?

—Yes.

—*Jazaakallah.*

He's still looking up at the sign like he's spooked. What is he looking at? I check it myself.

—You know where we're going? Dasghar? Jump in, I'll tell you...

I get in and turn the rig around—it's like the fates conspired to save that village idiot.

—I ain't all there, get me... But... if this is the same

Dasghar... I've got an uncle or someone there, I can't remember.

He's muttering his *dhikr*.

—Tha is Allah. Helping us. Those who help themselves. *Samje?* We may still save your Sufi hide, Baba.

He's muttering his *dhikr*.

—Whatever.

Those Mongol-eyed hillbillies staring after us: I'm thinking about the patrols or lookouts.

—I don't know whether we should ride together. We're conspicuous. Ya know? I mean you could jump out and blend right in. You could jump out here, *chattu*. You can jump, can't you? You can jump out here. I'm only doing twenty.

He's not biting.

—Aah, maybe there's a reason you're here. You sit tight, Baba. Your boy's gonna get you home.

I drive, sometimes like I'm back in the game, sometimes sick as hell.

Do you see it? The first small town on adjoining mountain.

I'm nodding off, but no point asking next man.

—I can't remember his name. I'm shagged, boss.

And then we get stuck behind a horse and cart. Like, what's it doing up here? We're throttling in second gear and I can't see anywhere to pass. I give it the horn and this farmer all bundled up—he doesn't turn around. The woman sitting next to him turns and just in that flash I see she's younger and it smacks me.

She doesn't look again and I'm tired something chronic. And I'm not so sure anymore. I mean raah, what if we find the place? I barely know this person.

—See that, boss?

There's tangles of wires looping across the goat hills and farmsteads on bent poles.

—Is that phone lines?

I floor it when there's a chance, with the sun starting to close the mountains.

Or did I pull off onto a steep track that climbs to a ravine quarry?

I hurt, I says.

And then I'm spark out on the wheel.

He's with a group of children shooting at tin cans in the desert. They're lying in soldierly position with air rifles but his skinny barrel bends to the right and as it pops the bullet veers off in an arc.

And then a steam train journey with no steam and no train, but winding rock candy cliffs shelved with blue and pink and lemon cottages with white picket fences; a longing pulling like luggage, and it was heaven.

I'm waking convinced I've seen my man and town. I'm waking cold.

The old man is looking at my bruises. My face is killing me. My leg is killing me.

—We should go in after dark. What you say? Or you go in first. I ain't even thought about how we get word to this guy. You speak their language, don't you? You speak their language. And we can't hang on to these wheels. Might just as well send up a flare. You don't think so?

I'm talking but my leg is killing me. And I'm cold.

—We should hide it. Coz blatant we been lucky so far. We should ditch it. You don't think so?

I can't tell if he's nodding or rocking.

—Yeah, well that's what we're doing. You speak their language, right?

Who knows what he's nodding at.

—Speak their language? You speak a language? You want to try?

He's watching from the bank while I reverse into an elbow of the ravine, with a clump of spiky trees veiling a drop into a quarry. It might hide it from the main road. I have my fight with the handbrake, then I climb into the back and it's got some boxes, and I try prising them open, but my hand is killing.

We get back down the track, followed by biting things. In an hour we'll need a torch.

I say, *We gotta be like ninja.*

We get near the road and a horse and cart come round. And I hear this grind and snapping, then a rumble. I'm thinking it's from the road. There's a crash, another crash, and I realise it's behind us.

The driver of the cart stands up and for a second all of us see the lorry fly off the track and disappear into the blind quarry.

We hear it smashing down, everything freezes—my blood, my skin, my breath—then there's this final crash.

No one saying nowt.

Did I put the brake on?

—I put the brake on.

There's a woman as well. They're all looking at me.

—I did!

And then something in the wreckage explodes.

Jazaakallah. This is a good place to kill myself.

Maybe dusk will hide it.

The farmer and woman are staring at us.

I says to the old man, *Tell them we had an accident.*

8

Black plumes billow from the brow of the pass. Maybe dusk will hide it.

I'm letting my man sort it out. He hardly looks at the farmer as they talk. The farmer he's got his daughter sitting next to him in a headscarf—I think it's his daughter. She's looking at us.

And I see this little motion from the farmer. And she signals me into the back of the cart. I can't climb over the side and my old geezer has to help. And I'm sure the farmer sees the iron band still round his ankle. And then she signals us to lie down.

We're down under a tarp with sacks of grain and turnipy things and a tied-up little goat.

A horse and cart. What's a horse and cart doing here?

A journey head down in a jawbreaking cart. The sky still polished blue. The black plumes rising. What is the deal? I don't know what the deal is.

This is it. We got no chance.

Perhaps the girl speaks softly with her father. The scrap of her voice so sweet it hurts.

—You couldn't ask him if they've got a phone, could you? Or if they've ever seen a phone.

I sound retarded with my mouth all banged up. And then tears well up. And I'm shivering.

—God damn.

I'm sure they can hear me heaving. And the girl passes a dark bottle. I drink water through loosened teeth, wetting broken lips and hair.

Evening swifts.

Her dad is talking to her. She suddenly says, You father?

—My father?

The girl nods.

—You father here?

—No.

She's still nodding. She's asking my man, probably who we are, how we got here. And when he answers in his slow way I realise he's not a native speaker.

—No father?

—No. Gone. Gone... Long time. I never...

—Here?

I'm looking at my broken watch.

—This is all I've got.

Why do I even say that?

The farmer says something and she seems to translate.

—Your father country this?

—Yes. No. Not exactly.

—You what country?

The bottle is maybe green in this light. I take another swig, cover my face. I never want this cart to stop.

There was a text on his mobile with the first word in capitals: 'BAILIFF due to remove your GOODS. Call MICHAEL on 01604 331901 to STOP action. Do Not Text.' There was the miserable fear again, no matter where he ran. But it couldn't be a real distraint, there was no court order.

A woman dripping boredom is on the other end.

What's it about, he asks.

I need you to confirm your address for me, please.

Yeah, but what's it about?

I need you to confirm your address.

I don't know what it's about. I don't think it's me.

Are you Rashid Naseeb or Naseeb Rashid?

Yeah.

Which one?

Naseeb.

Naseeb Rashid?

Yeah. What's this for? I got a message saying something.

I need you to confirm your address for me, please.

I don't know if I'm awake. I'm thinking I've got a phone in my hand. I can hear the truck in my ear. I can hear the dripping water of that prison box.

The sky is darker. And the drool has run out my mashed-up mouth.

My lips split open.

Soft drumming on the frame of this cart.

Then it pings my ear, my head.

I try to straighten up but my ankle is fucked. I crane my face to the trickle. Drops still vibrate.

There's a dark patch where I've been lying. It's falling on the board behind the farmer. A flask or a bottle leaking. The tail of the farmer's tattered jacket is darkened.

In the last light I see blood drip from the jacket.

I feel my face and the drool.

—I think our friend here is bleeding.

No one looks at me.

—Did you hear me? Ask him why he's—

Another drip. I'm reaching up to the bloke's arm.

—You're bleeding.

And I says to her, *He's bleeding.*

Don't all rush—I can't be doing with this. I'm kneeling to look at tears in the back of the jacket. My gormless Dada watches me lift his jacket and the man's shirt and back is lashed to shreds.

—What the fuck is that! Did someone do that?

Maybe they're ashamed.

—Is he just gonna sit there?

Oh Jeez, they're all at it—the girl the farmer my man— following something on the wind not there.

But there are lights approaching from the distant mountain town. A jeep? And the farmer mutters to my man. The old man pulls the tarp around us, pulls me, motions *down, down.*

The motor's getting louder over the clatter of the cart. I pick my head up again and the farmer and his girl have got their eyes shut. And then the headlights start slinking through the cart sides. The noise is rattling the cart to break, and the goat starts thrashing and bleating. I think I see man and daughter bend right down in sajda. And I gotta look—through a crack in the cart side in the dark—I see insane shapes before they roar away in the jeep.

The cart lurches on into the quiet.

There's a flare endlessly dropping in my head...

... a woman half-buried in the roadside... her shattered face...

darkened dirt feeding late insects…

I think I woke up.

… a memory of trees overhead, and stars in the dizzying sky. At some time a hurricane lantern is lifted from the side of the cart, throwing shadows around.

A farmhouse standing in the western glow.

The town lights are still pricking the mountain.

I can't get out of the cart, and the old man barely makes it, so the farmer lugs the goat off, and then me.

We follow him with the girl lighting the way over the ruts up to the doorway, blocked with rusting things and useful things and broken. I can't tell if the low porch is wood or earth or brick. We wait in darkness in the hall. She comes back in the halo of an oil lamp, and leads us through a passage into this long room lit by a faint bulb in a doorframe.

Floor seating around the walls with oblong cushions and killims. The farmer is signalling to relax and then we're alone.

The old man lowers himself with huge sighs, and feeling his leg iron sores. As soon as I go to bend I've cramped, so I'm standing at the window. Up on a ridge there's the shadow of a derelict house.

—We could get these people in trouble.

My man is patting a cushion for me. I circle the carpet, and try again and lie there groaning through the cramps.

9

Did I sleep?

I'm coughing like I did. This wait is doing my head in. I don't know anything.

—We could have got them in trouble. *Samje?*

My man has got his eyes closed, his *tasbih* on a roll.

—We have to find my uncle. Can you go into town? I'm too conspicuous. Too... foreigner... You speak their language right?

My man has got his *tasbih* on a roll.

And then I'm dangling my Casio in front of him in the dingy bulb light. He's got his old man's eye on it.

—Someone gave me this. Got his initials on the back. Maybe it's my uncle. You can read it.

I can't see shit in this light. How do I know it's my uncle's? My man he's squinting at a sliver of Urdu on the casing. I'm letting him read it, coz I'm not sure.

Did I sleep? I'm trying not to think they've gone to grass me up.

And then the farmer comes in with a bowl of muck. I

thought it was to eat. But he sits by me and signs to take my shirt off.

—I don't think I can move my arm. Here. My shoulder. Yeah. Can't move it. Can you help me? Shoulder, see? Can you help me. Yeah, it's like seized up. My head is a bb-iitch. Yeah, can you help me take this off?

He's feeling all my bumps and bruises. I say:

—I can't see straight out of this eye. It's like there's Vaseline inside. I think they... yeah. I can't move my...

He gives me four tablets. Then he kneads the muck in his hand into a ball and he starts laying these cowpats all over my body and head. He's a gnarly thing and his hands are still moiled from goatshit or potato picking or whatever they do here. Maybe he's putting it on his own back.

The daughter comes in to put out glasses and rock sugar. She's more careful with her headscarf. And she disappears behind these lattice screens fretted with the pattern of vine leaves or ripples on a pond or a mesh fence. I look at them and they flip patterns.

And then the men are drinking tea. Her dad drinks with long sighs. He could be bleeding to death for all I know. And I've got a cowpat on my skull and some greasy shit on my mouth and eye, and more of these cowpats on my arms and leg.

I'm looking at my Dada, trying to telepath him: We've got these people in trouble.

She comes with dishes of food. But I can't eat the flat bread or the dough balls or the fruit.

—I've got a tooth. I've got—gap. I've got a... I dunno, they must have... must have... See—wobbly, wobbly.

I'm sipping my tea. I hear the farmer say Amal to the girl.

She comes back with more dishes and puts it in front of me.

—This you say *chana*?

—Yeah.

—Yes. This you say...?

—Maybe it's *bengan*. Aubergine.

—Yes.

And her father is doing the *eat, eat* with his hand.

I pat my chest, *I'm Naseeb.*

Yes, she says.

—You speak English.

She keeps her head down and gives it a little shake.

—No? Sounded like English. Do you have a name?

Her father speaks to her and I think I've offended him.

She says, *You stay?*

And the old man looks at me.

—Thank you, uncle. But it would be too much trouble.

The farmer looks to her and they talk. I hear him say Amal again.

She says, You stay. The scrap of her voice so sweet it hurts.

—Thank you, but it's too much trouble.

—Not trouble.

No trouble? And what is my Baba saying? Is that a nod? And her dad mimes putting his head on a pillow.

—We'd really appreciate if we could rest. And then we have to go.

—You stay?

—Yes. Can I ask how far the border is? Border?

—No. Alone no.

—What?

But she's gone. Then the old timer's talking to the farmer. I hear the farmer call him *Haji Bey*, and he's tapping the killim with his finger, and the fingers snap out into a fan, and he's shaking his head.

And my bones won't move anymore.

Did we finish eating?

They wake me to go to bed. The poultices are dried solid and pinching my skin. And the farmer leads us across the yard to a shack that smells of livestock, and points to the outhouse and leaves a lamp made of rust.

The only thing my man asks is, *Qibla?*

I've gone to the outhouse with the hurricane lamp under a spray of stars. And when I'm squatting on my heels inside I can hear the blood pumping in my head, and my cough explode in the walls. And there's a constant rumble of roadworks in the distance. And I turn my head this way, that way, to wipe away the sound for a moment before it swims back in. And the cowpats crack on my legs and back. And I can't think about any of it.

And afterwards I'm looking up at the stars and I can't make any sense.

And the farmer comes shuffling up. He's saying something, pointing across the slopes, and I get the idea I'm not supposed to stray.

The shack is brick and mud. And a long table bed with mattress rolls. In this light I don't have to worry about the ratshit I'll find in the morning. I crawl onto my side of the bed. My man is standing with his back to me.

—What's your name, Baba?

But Baba is standing for *salat.*

And for the first time I've remembered Abba. But I could be dreaming.

I sleep with the whole weight of the sky on me.

It sounded like the same woman. She quoted the reference number and brings up the case.

She says, Council Tax.

But we did a payment schedule with the council.

When was this?

That's what I'm saying. We got a letter for a payment schedule.

Do you have the letter there?

I'm not there right now. I'm gonna be back Sunday.

He called back to give the schedule.

And she said, And is your address 67 Warstone Road?

No, it's 12 Gladesmere.

I've got here your address is 67 Warstone Road. Are you N Rashid?

Wait... I got this message... I don't know what it's...

Have you ever lived at 67 Warstone Road?

No, it's not me.

10

By the light that leaks between tin roof and wall.

And the timber struts discernible.

And the young man who lies coughing on his side.

I lay down after my night prayers and a sleep like death lay on me. We have not moved since falling in crushing sleep. What time is this?

I cannot do your service Allah. My tongue moves but I have forgotten You. There was a time when my heart was alive. Help me to remember Allah.

The shutters are closed, the door is closed. The creatures are fed and milked. And still we sleep.

I can do nothing. Each day I pray for the power to do, may You guide me. But Shaytan whispers that my sloth is surrender.

Opening the door the sun is high.

I watch for a sign on the mountain road below or on the uplands. The broken teeth on the night ridge are now a tiny derelict building.

Do you hear that creaking pump behind the house?

I look around that wall. The girl pulls her ablutions from

the pump with one hand. I realize her headscarf is down. And even for a vanishing moment—look! That side of her face so wealed with livid gashes!

I return from the outhouse, my *wudhu* made in a bucket.

The boy wakes as I pray. My tongue moves but I have forgotten.

And afterwards he says, I don't want to lie to them.

And after a time he says, You don't think we should tell them?

The girl calls us.

—You're right—we should keep them out of it.

They give the boy a barley broth and a soft bread he can soak.

—I feel loads better. My body—much better, sir. This— this—very good. Your medicine—very good.

Ghaffar bey sits smoking. There is no sign he is wounded. He asks about our belongings, and I shake my head.

He says: *Where were you going, Haji Bey?*

And I say, *To the border*, and tilt my head in such a way that he asks no more.

Perhaps Naseeb understood something. He says:

—Uncle. How far is the border?

Ghaffar bey makes a sign with his hand—over there, the border.

—Border. How far?

Ghaffar bey asks me, *Which way are you going?*

And the boy says, Other side.

Ghaffar bey understands something, he uses his hand, going round in a big curve: *Tuk-tuk-tuk-tuk-tuk-tuk...*

He holds out the fingers of one hand and makes an 'O' with the other.

—*Five.*

He emphasises the 'O' hand.

—Fifty, says Naseeb.

—Da.

—Fifty what? Miles? Kilometres?

—Ha.

—What? Miles?

—Da.

—Or kilometres?

—Ha.

After a pause Ghaffar bey says, Yes.

Naseeb asks me, What did he say?

—He said Yes.

And he says, *Jazaakallah.*

I stretch my hand for the boy's watch. I say, Your uncle's

name?

—I don't know... Ghalib Khan.

—*Ghaffar bey, this boy has an uncle somewhere here. His name is Ghalib Khan. His uncle will know this watch.*

Ghaffar bey takes the watch and I point out the mark on the inside. Do you see? He squints for an inscription in a cheap digital watch.

They clean the boy's wounds and put us in a brick bathroom with a trough in the wall and pots of hot water. And I wash him.

Do you see the boy looking in a stained mirror? Do you see him afraid? I see my face and I do not know it.

Then they lay on his poultices again. And the boy says:

—This medicine—very good. Natural. Big companies, they want you to buy a million aspirins.

And they give us farm clothes. And the girl says:

—You please stay here. Not outside.

Then they are gone to their work, and we are alone. And the boy says, Do we sit here?

We sit and our thoughts wander labyrinths that never reach an end and never discover the beginning.

I am too tired to rest.

And there is no end.

11

By the time.

The farmer comes back, and we hear sounds in a kitchen. And he asks me to lead *zuhr*. And the four of us stand.

Pray? What should I pray? My tongue moves but I have forgotten You. Help me to remember, Allah. I cover myself in forgetfulness before each iota of good and bad is made to speak. Oh Allah, may You hide our sins.

—*Assalaamualaykum wa rahmatullah. Assalaamualaykum wa rahmatullah.*

There is a stew with doughballs, and more tablets for Naseeb.

I see him looking at Ghaffar bey: if he has imagined the flagellant wounds, if there is another explanation for the bloody shreds.

She clears away and returns with a soft, dog-eared text book, and she puts it in front of the boy and opens a page. And she says, *You please correct my English.*

She slips behind the wooden screens fretted with arabesque leaves or wavelets. And the boy sits there bewildered. Her father says, *Ingliz, Ingliz,* and urges him to open the book.

The boy stares at the book but doesn't see it. Then her voice comes from behind the screen:

—*Hello, my name is Serena. I live in Kashkar. My father's name is Ahmed. You may please correct my English.*

The boy stares at the screen. But her father is nodding and his hands urging.

—I say this correct?

The boy nods unsurely, then makes an unsure sound. And she recites again:

—Thank you. I have also lee-arnt to read and write English.

Again he nods.

—Very good, she says. Where do you stay?

And he is looking at the page. She answers for him:

—You are staying in Arif Hotel? Is it a good hotel?

The boy stares at the screen with its patient shadow behind it, and at the page, and he reads carefully:

—The hotel is quite... good?

—Are you married?

The boy is reading from his place:

—Yes. I have got a two-year-old son.

—Are they also here?

—No, they are in London now.

—Tomorrow is a holiday. Why don't you come and have lunch with us?

The boy looks at me, but she is waiting for his answer. And he reads:

—Thank you, but would it—wouldn't it be too much of a bother?

—Not at all! My wife will be very ple-ased.

And he checks the text.

—It's *plee-sed.*

—My wife will be very pleased.

—Okay. We'll meet tomorrow.

—What is your address?

—Here is my card. Come around twelve.

—Okay. Salaam.

And they fall still. Ghaffar bey smokes, his eyes far away, rocking gently.

And Naseeb—he leans over the pages and mouths more words to himself. That boy, he looks at something in his mind. Finally he says:

—I can read this.

Ghaffar bey stirs himself, he motions to them to continue, *Da, da.*

She says, *Somebody is coming for lunch today.*

And he reads, *Who is coming?*

—My husband's new free-end, Mister—

—It's *friend.*

—My husband's new friend, Mister Robert Boon.

—Is that me? he says, and he reads: I feel tempted to come. Shall I come too?

—Yes, certainly do come.

The boy is smiling at his book:

—I can read this...

—What is your name?

He checks in the book but it must be her own question.

—Naseeb.

—Naseeb. And what is your occupation?

—I'm a... student. I'm not working. I'm travelling. And you? Sister.

—I am... help my father.

—*Hamdulillah, hamdulillah...* Have you always helped him?

And there is a silence. The boy looks at me and Ghaffer bey.

—Have you always been on the farm? Did you go to school?

—I... I...

She seems unsure.

He thinks perhaps his questions are unsafe.

—My folks call me Jahan. That's like 'guided', can you believe. In Urdu. No, it's 'world'. Or something. Do you know Urdu? My mom calls me... Naseeb... Rashid...

And my name... I try to remember.

—Your father name is Rashid.

—Yes. No. Rashid... Yeah... I can't remember. I think they kicked my...

That boy, he looks at something in his mind.

—My name is Amal. This is my father.

—Sister, I want to be up front with you. I think we could get you in serious trouble. You've been really kind, *hamdulillah*. But we could get you...

He looks at Ghaffar bey.

—... trouble.

They look back patiently. She says, No trouble.

—Sister, I hope you don't mind. If I ask you something. I can't get my head around your father. What's that about? His back. Did someone do that? Who would do that? Is it an accident?

Her eyes are lowered and her father's eyes are on her.

—I've seen things here... I don't understand this place.

Does anyone know about this? I mean outside of your country. Do people think they deserve this? It doesn't have to be this way. You don't have to live like this. Who's doing this?

After a long pause she says, We do this.

—Is there a war going on? It doesn't have to be this way. It gets me completely... when I see good people have to live like this. I'm really sorry if we cause trouble for you. If we're not supposed to be here.

—No trouble.

—Wallahi, I would never put you in danger. I'd give my life first. I wish I could help. I really do. Is there anything I could do? People should fight. Are they doing that? They should.

And then everyone falls silent.

Ghaffar bey signs to me:

—*We will find your man tonight. I give the watch to someone. Yes.

What is this language he speaks? That I understand. And I tell Naseeb what he said.

Ghaffar bey beckons us to follow him out. We stoop when we hear a vehicle on the road. And from behind the outhouse he points high up the ridge with specks of goats or sheep pricking the slope and above them a stub of a shelter.

And he shouts up to the slope for Umid and tells him he's

to collect something. And there's a faint reply but I cannot see them.

—*You give the watch to Umid. You see there? I will take you there tonight. You stay in that shelter. You understand? Wait there for whoever comes.

I understand and tell Naseeb who thinks we're to go now and makes a step. And the farmer snatches him back.

—*I will take you.

And he starts ushering us back to the house.

—Let me pray nafl here, I say.

And I signal salat to Ghaffar bey. And he urges me inside, No, no, no.

—*I have been inside for a very long time, I say.

—Baba geezer, don't be mental. We're supposed to be ninja.

—Allah will protect us.

—What, protect us back to prison?

—*Haji baba, you cannot go beyond this bound.

—*I am just praying. La hawla wala quwwata illa billah. Please.

And finally Ghaffar bey says, La hawla wala quwwata illa billah. And he ushers Naseeb back to the house.

Nafl? Why do I pray nafl? Because I fear I am faithless?

I am waiting for Huu to speak through this vessel. Everywhere the gnats are wavering on Your breath, the mosquitoes bite to remind me. But each second weighs my shame. Shame, Allah!

I hardly know that I'm climbing the slopes.

The mountains had dragged a cloak of clouds across the sky. How dark their sheet. Two hollows in the billow of clouds make the sockets of a face; it slides into a similitude.

I hardly know I'm climbing the slopes.

And I see a face as of a reflection in a well—two smudges and falling hair, and the face is young. Yes, a holy fool! I see You, Allah. And as I look the smudges become crestfallen. Here I lie on the slope with the goats and see the grand sweep of a wave rushing with outstretched arms and a huge gaping mask. *Subhanallah* how serene these skies that are not yet molten brass, of mountains not yet tossed as wool!

The mouth of the flying head widens and is about to speak; and another head joins and enters it, slowly diving into the temple like a twin; and the face turns back to chaos.

And I hear the chant of Umid calling the clinking goats. A child's voice. When he's closer I beckon the boy.

He holds onto a shaggy goat bigger than him, as if I wanted to steal it. I say, perhaps in his tongue, *Where are you taking them?

He mumbles something and points somewhere.

—*Is that your home there, I say, pointing to the distant town.*

He shakes his head, but he is confused. I look on this child in his waistcoat and woven skullcap and I take out the watch.

—*Khan... Do you know a Khan? Is there Khan in your village? This watch belongs to Ghalib Khan.*

He puts down his goat and takes the watch, and I look on this child with his waistcoat and woven cap and uncomprehending face.

—*His kin is here to see him.*

He asks if it's Ghaffer uncle's kin, he doesn't know this person.

I say, *It is in Allah's hands. Go. Ghaffar bey says go.*

And he turns to catch his goat, and my heart lurches in its cage and is beating in my throat. For his waistcoat is slashed and the shirt is slashed and bloodied, and flies dance on his shirt. And he catches his goat and climbs the slope to his flock. And starts whistling them to the dip. And a bird is beating in my throat.

Ya Allah, what are these hands shaking for? What are they to do?

I prostrate on the slope that leaps to meet my brow,

without *wudhu*, without *qiyam*.

How long do I swoon?

The goats are sounding still.

Help me to remember You, Allah. As many times I prostrated I have not prostrated. I meditate my sins yet I cannot find my sins.

Subhanallah. Subhanallah. Subhanallah. Subhanallah.

Listen, that distant drone in my ear after the engine was switched off.

Or a faint rhythmic chanting.

Is it from the valley? Or the other side of the mountain?

And a drum joined to it.

I press my ear to the ground—

—the *dhikr* pulses in the earth—can you hear voices? the ringing of a daf?... and it thunders in my head, as though I were in the dhikr circle.

The howling music fills the valley—

How long do I swoon?

A weight slams on my shoulder, a hand with the heft of a mountain! A hand slams on my shoulder and the thunder of *dhikr* is gone, and fear is in my throat—

Naseeb is staring wildeyed at me.

He hisses, *What the hell are you doing?* And checking if

anyone is around.

—What are you doing up here?

—I make *du'a*.

—Fuck *du'a*! You just stuck yourself on show for everyone to see. What are you doing!

—I give the watch to the boy.

—You give the—? No you didn't! You give the watch—? You didn't think to tell me?

—The boy will find your uncle.

—What did you tell him?

—Your uncle will come.

Can you hear the sound of a vehicle growling from far? And the boy looks wildeyed across the scant tree line of the farm boundary. And he starts slipping down the hill on his belly looking wildeyed at me, and hissing:

—Awwhhgh! Old man! You are here to fuck me up! You are here to fuck us all up!

Until the rumble of the vehicle is close and he lies facedown on the slope and holds his head as if this will hide him.

Until the vehicle is rumbling away, and I can just hear him:

—You Haji halfwit.

And he starts slithering up the slope again.

I say, Your uncle will come.

—Where's that *bakri chod*? Where'd he go!

The goats are sounding still. And he stands up and tries to run across the slope.

Listen!

A sharp crack explodes beyond the dip, that ricochets after an age across the valley. And panicked bleating, and crows scuttling away, and white smoke low in the dip.

And we look at each other and wonder *Is that the goatherd or the goat?*

12

Banchod, I drag that deadbeat back, where Amal and her dad are praying. Did they hear it? I can't say nuffink. And he just sits with his *tasbih*. Had enough *namaz*, then. I'm so wound up, blatant, I cannot trust myself to talk. They must have heard it.

And then she disappears behind the screen again. And her shadow moves behind leaves or stars or waves.

My chest is burning. I'm fingering the book all spaced out, and I can't tell what is English and what is foreign.

I hear her voice behind the screen.

—Salaam.

I say *Salaam* back.

—You are Robert Boon?

Finally I say, *Did you hear anything just?*

And there's another long silence.

—You are Robert Boon?

I don't know if I can do this, but her dad is going *Da, da, Ingliz, Ingliz,* and I find the place. It says, *Salaam. I am Robert Boon. What is your name?* And I'm fingering the letters, like I don't know if they're English.

—Da, da, says her dad.

—I admire you all, you know. It's good she's still learning. Good, sir. *I am Robert Boon. I am with the British Council. And you?*

—I teach history in the university.

—Yeah. I don't know... me and education... Do you have a post office? Somewhere to send letters?

She says, *Letter? Write letter?*

—No wait. They're going to trace it here. How can we get word out? Without signposting where it's from. It has to be far from here.

Her dad is asking her what I'm saying, and then he's talking to my man. And then Ghaffer *chacha* goes and gets paper and pen. And my man says:

—Write the letter. If your uncle comes he can find a way.

They're all looking at me. I'm looking at this piece of paper. And like my hand is fiddling air.

They're all looking at me.

—I hate writing letters... What should I say?... Tell them I'm in hiding. Yeah. Tell them I'm a British citizen. There must be records. Who I am.

And I have a horror that I'm not sure of my name or how I got here, and I look at my pen nib scratching air.

And I hear the sweet voice of the girl:

—Your name is Nacip...

—Yeah. Naseeb. My dad calls me... My dad... I don't know what his name is.

And for the first time I remember Abba. I'm sitting in A&E with Baba, and that's Arif—they're looking on, hurting for me. My dad's saying, *You want more painkiller, more painkiller, boy?* I keep saying no, and then the nurse goes to sew up my mouth and Baba says, *You want without?* And I say, Yeah. And the nurse, she has to sew it up without an anaesthetic, with Baba and Arif looking on.

And I get a lump in my throat, I want my family to know.

And I'm trying to remember Mom.

But I see the dogs, in the upstairs floorboards, with this crew going apeshit, and the dogs gone apeshit, and they're clamped together flecking foam—we're shouting *Yes, Milo! Fuck him up, boy! Yes-yes!* Those devil dogs surging up from the filthy carpet, ripping cheek and lip. And me I'm giving it like I'm hard, but I'm not feeling it. And that dog, he gets merked, and there's a bucket brought up to clean the blood, and a yellow Ikea bag for the dog. And I'm carrying it out to the delivery car when the stupid dog struggles out and hobbles squealing down the road. I'm running after it, and it's looking back, I'm calling him but he's never coming back.

I don't know whose these memories are. I don't know why they're all shit. I'm trying to remember Mom.

And I nearly remember the girls on the mattresses, and my heart hammers the blood in my face.

Why is it all so shit? I'm not this. I got a letter to write.

I look at Amal behind the lattice screen like an endless fence with interlinking arms, and her shadow shifting, shifting—I want her to make it all right, I want her to reach through those eyelets and put her hand in my head and wash these thoughts.

I know what Old MacDonald is mumbling, he's saying *Write, write your letter, everything is good.* Or something.

My pen is scratching air.

—I know I've done a lot of bad things probably. What do you think I should say? I don't know anything.

My Haji chief, he bows his head and sighs.

—Write.

And my gammy hand starts writing, *To Whom It May Concern*, and I'm looking at my hand sweeping the page, and I see the words but I don't rightly know what's coming.

Afterwards I stare at the page. Shining with *barakah*.

It's only taken me four years.

My man and Ghaffer bey they're still talking, and then

Haji says to me, *We should eat, and then go to our meeting place.*

And instead of eating, they get ready to pray.

And Ghaffer bey gives the *azan*, and the old man says *Fatiha*. And I feel her praying behind us.

And my man is crying in the *du'a*—forgive us this and forgive us that, forgive us if we made a mistake in *salat*, and his voice is breaking higher—forgive us if we blew your little friend up. And her dad is crying—forgive us if we didn't wash between our toes. And she joins in, weeping *Yallah*.

And here's a man on the hospital bed, his face caved in and the mouth dragged down, and the eyes just shrunken puddles. I remember his silvery chest. That hurt me most, because I recognized me own—it rasped up and down. It doesn't look like Abba. But I dunno what Abba looks like.

And I think it would be good to join in and cry on cue. With the old man wailing something about *Why did you leave us like this?* It would be good to cry with her.

Look. I'm crying. A man on a hospital bed. He wants to go toilet.

What's happening to me? I've turned into a heaving fit, and I can't stop crying, while they're blarting on and on, *Why'd you leave us like this? We need your help.* I can't stop, and I don't know who is thinking in my head and I'm scared of this body.

Afterwards I go and wash my face, and I'm scared of this face with the battered eyes and teeth.

So she lays out more of the *bengan* and broth and yoghurt and a big watermelon. And the only thing said is, the old man he says, *Ghaffer bey has put word out in the morning.*

And when we're saying goodbye she's there at the doorway.

She's there at the doorway, careless with her headscarf. And every time she looks at her father I see her face. In the rusty bulb light, jagged shadows across her face, shadows like weals or scars.

I see her face and she doesn't care.

I say, *Assalam alaykum. Please thank your father for everything. May Allah taala bless you.*

She says, *Please pray for us.*

—I'll pray for you. I pray we can meet in more happy time. Meet, more happy.

—Inshaallah.

13

Up here it's still light. We hardly need the torch.

Ghaffer bey leads and we start making the climb, with two plastic bottles of water, up the scarp that slides beneath us. The letter in my pocket burning with hope.

My gammed-up leg. I can't get rid of this cough. Maybe it was the prison, maybe it was the mountain. My man is silent, not a grunt, not a sigh.

More and more lights come on across the valley. And down below I can see a slow light moving in the courtyards of the farm, the livestock bleating, and she must be bringing the goats and chickens inside.

My Haji, he's had a nice long rest in prison, because he's climbing this mountain like a billy goat.

I'm scared the letter will fly out my pocket.

My head is clear.

I can see that man in the hospital... my Dad... when he wanted me and Arif... Arif, yeah. When he wanted me and Arif to take him to the toilet, but the doctors have got him all hooked up.

My bastard leg. Lugging a bottle of water.

I'm trying to remember Mom. I know her name. But I can't see her. She's like this breeze in the curtains.

And I don't know if this is the same time—(what do we call her?)—when she comes in Arif gets up and turns to the wall. Maybe it's not our mother—she's goore.

Then Ghaffer bey stops and gives a hurricane lamp to my man and starts going on and on and pointing over the ridge. And he comes down to me and does the same but adding *Dis way, dis way*, like that makes all the difference.

And he's leaving us.

—*Allah hafiz.*

The ruined shelter silhouetted like broken teeth. Who knows what it's doing up there?

We get up there and I realize I don't know what's supposed to happen.

Stone, earthwork, half the roof gone, the timber still up, and there's a rough window looking out over the valley. Up here it's still light.

My *dada* sets the hurricane lamp inside. A blue tongue of flame.

—What are we doing here, uncle?

—Your friend will come.

—You think one of the goats got through?

—He will come.

—And then what?

I sit against the outer wall to look down the valley, and the sky with polished wracks, the sky with the Dog Star, or is it Venus?

Rip Van Winkle he props up inside. I can hear his back rasp behind me.

It's getting dark.

—What's your name, uncle?

And just when I've forgotten about him, he says:

—I don't know.

Am I surprised?

—Well what can you remember?

Back to back, each side of a wall, trying to remember our names.

But I'm thinking how to get a fixer, get the letter out, steal some wheels, find a route.

What the hell is the time?

My arse is freezing. They could follow my coughing from the other side of the valley.

I hunker inside from the cold where darkness covers the walls and rubble of the low floor, until I get used to the lantern light and stars in the roof.

And I'm just dozing off when Old Father Time says:

—I remember... a boy playing in snow with another child. And an older boy kicked the palace they were building. And the boy knew he must act, and he pushed the older one's face in the snow without fear. Allah is Bestower.

—So was that boy you?

I wait so long I might as well be talking to the wall.

14

I wake with the hurricane lamp throwing shadows on a man with silvery chest dying in a hospital like a bombed-out school house.

I'm alone and the hole in the roof is dark with stars.

Outside, my spar is harkening to unearthly things on the wind. I don't know if he hears it or smells it. And I go quiet and seem to hear it too.

—What is that?

And the faint howl is gone. Or never there.

I'm holding my breath.

—It's the sound of my screw coming loose. I'm as nuts as you are. You happy now?

The night has come. The constellations slide through the roof.

And now I'm thinking what if someone comes.

If no one came I wouldn't be worried. If no one came I could sleep. Perhaps go back to Amal's.

If someone came I've got no tool, no blammer. Gotta rely on Dad's Army here.

I've found myself an iron door flange to swing. And we stand looking out of the broken panes of the window.

In the long silence I say:

—Do you think we'll get out of here?

And he says:

—This is Barzakh.

And it doesn't sound stupid anymore.

We see the lights of three vehicles in all our watch. And sometimes a wailing on the wind.

I think I'm awake, but when the old man's hand touches my arm I wake up still on my feet.

And there's noise in the slopes. We hear it scrabble and trip stones or, I don't know, I've caught my breath hoping it's nothing.

There it scurries.

My man presses my arm and he creeps to the door and out. I'm at the window ready to brain the first thing that comes in.

There's my man's shape in the gloom.

And then everything runs cold when I hear this low gutteral growl.

And my man is singing, a singsong word, like an Okay, like Easy, whatever he's saying, one long singsong.

I'm waiting for time with my blood gone cold.

He comes back and says nothing.

—Well?

—A dog.

This is Barzakh. It's probably a fucking werewolf.

My nerves get shredded listening—livestock blorting, foxes shrieking murder, scuttling around the shelter.

We haven't seen a vehicle light for...

What is the time?

There's more scrabbling up the scarp.

I get noiselessly up to the door with the heft of the iron bar.

A sweet voice.

I come out the door and there's her shadow climbing up.

Oh my days.

And my man has come out too. And I'm like, *What are you doing? You shouldn't have come. Does your dad know?*

—I find you, she says.

I'm looking around just in case.

—You shouldn't have come. You understand?

—Yes. I bring you things. *Assalamalaykum,* she says to my man.

She takes out a couple of shawls from her rucksack, a flask

of something. And looking down she gives me a *tasbih* smooth like agate.

All the guff I keep giving, *You mustn't stay, it could bring trouble*—I want her to stay. As long as possible.

We stay in the open out of *adab*. And she and the old man squat against the wall and talk. When it should be me. Perhaps he'll talk her down.

So I shamble around the shelter on lookout like a noddy.

I'm trying not to think of her.

I'm trying to remember Mom. It's like looking at my life through a crack in the wall.

Is that her? There, sitting with the menfolk in her cotton frock and bare arms; me, sitting on the sofa arm next to her, afraid to be alone with them. And she talks to them like they'd be interested in what she said. And the *Bibis* talk to her to cover her shame. She's talking about bowel cancer as though they'd understand, but when they say *Allah hayat*, she understands.

Amal says: *He will come.*

I say, *I don't even know who he is.*

—He will come.

—And what if he doesn't?

—Everything may be good.

What do you say to that?

—Can he take us across the border?

—Not worry.

—Say if he can't—is there a way? Do you know a way?

And then she talks softly to the Haji, and he's shaking his head, looks ready to go back to jail. But she gets up and is lighting the way further up the slope.

—I show.

She keeps saying, *I show, just show*, while we drag ourselves up the tough, short stretch to the crest.

I'm going ahead of Dad's Army.

A pale desert plane. Snatches of wailing rhythmic howling on the wind.

She steps along the crest then shines her lantern low. A track? I would never have noticed it.

—Does that go all the way down?

—This way, she says, then points beyond the desert:

—This way... maybe twenty mile. Half day. Straight. Not in day.

—Not a whole day.

—Not in day you go. In night. Must be in night.

It shines eerily in the dark bounds of mountains. And higher than the valley behind us.

—This way?

—This star.

She points at something in a spray of stars.

—You go this way star.

—Down there? This way?

And my man is talking to her, his hand fans the sky. I can guess. Even I know the sky will be moving in the night. But her hand points firmly to one part of the sky.

I say, *Which star?*

—This called *Ship* stars. This stars.

And she makes a square shape with her hands, and she's pointing. I'm saying, *That one?*

She's saying *Hah, hah.*

But I don't see a ship.

—But you must now go. Long time down. And after, walking six, seven hour. Must go before morning.

And my man talks some more and she's making signs beyond—a hand chopping across her other hand, her hands pointing parallel—and my man explains there is a border road, but we must find another place to cross.

And I try a few steps down the incline. It's not so steep. The desert is shining softly. But the mountain pitched in darkness. And they would see us from Mars in daylight.

—We still have to meet this bloke.

She says, *Ha.*

And then nobody says anything.

—I don't know what I did… I've done a lot of bad things I'm sure.

She says, *You do something bad.*

—Not this time! It's some… giant mistake. I just have to get back.

—You are good man, says Amal.

—We should go, says my man.

I don't know if he means the desert or the shack.

And then she says:

—I go. You go. He goes. They all go.

Still no one goes.

—Next time you will visit with Mrs Boon.

And I'm looking up at her face, and I'm ready to cry. So I say:

—She is certainly welcome.

And she says, *What would Mrs Boon like to eat?*

—What do you think she would like to eat?

And I think the black hole of her face is looking straight at me. And she recites from memory:

—I won't cook too many dishes. I'll make fish fry, meatballs and bread. And for your son…

—What will you give my son?

—I am thinking of serving rice pudding.

I can't think of anything else.

And Old Father Time says, *We should go.* And disappears back down the ridge.

Amal lights the way for me.

I can't think of anything else. I want to say any old chat, *I was thinking what you said, about being responsible for things...* And here come half-familiar voices like flies buzzing in the curtains.

I want to hear her voice like so gentle it hurts.

Here come voices buzzing in my head:

That's right, you go! He's got to go, Nate. Big bad man is going to let you protect me. Oh! Who's that on the phone?

I'm there in a passage getting my jacket yanked off—

An you're gonna leave? You're just gonna up and fuckin leave! Yeah go on! Go on! That's you innit! Bring shooters here an leave stupid Leesh to sort it out. That's what she deserves.

I want to say stuff to Amal, *I can understand, coz in the West, we give arms to dictators, and stand by and do nothing when they oppress people...*

And my head is hammering, and my creps slithering down the slope—

You're not going! You're gonna face it with me. Are you going to leave him like this? Are you!

We find *Haji* sat against the wall. And he says something to her—like maybe she should go now.

But she's giving us tea.

How long should we wait for this geezer? No one says.

My head is leaking. And I go inside the shelter and stand by the window. And I hang on to her *tasbih*.

My head is leaking shit, of me smoking crack with some next man. And I'm going like, *Yeah, Camel, let's go masjid, yeah? Camel, let's go masjid!*

I'm trying to shake this buzzing out of my head, I want to cry again, when I realise she's outside the window.

I'm not breathing.

I think she's outside the window.

The pinprick lights in the black valley. The far-off foxes shrieking murder and the dogs yapping.

How long should we wait?

And it's like this other voice is saying to the darkness:

—It's good that you're with your father. That you're close. I wanted to stay with Abba, you know. Be more like him. But I started getting nicked. To be honest I don't know where half my life went. I might as well have been dead.

Is she listening?

—My mom's name is Sara. Yeah, I went to her house after Young Offenders, and... she's got this piano, and, I'm just touching the keys—and I can't play for toffee—but she says, *Don't stop, you play beautifully.*

I remember it, the smell of dark wood. Arif touching the cake, she smacks his hand, *Don't touch food.*

You play beautifully.

When did I get nicked?

And then she cooks chips and Arif asks if it's cooked in lard. The dick. *Don't be silly*, she says, and he has to eat it with a face like puke.

Who was the bloke?

He never forgave her.

I can hear Amal listening. She may not want to hear but I have to say this—

—I think I've got a sprog. A boy. Yeah. I know I've got one. I think I've got one. He's with his mother. Yeah. She's a good woman. A good mother. She's a good mother. So I got no worries.

It's all right. She's letting me talk.

—I mean blatant, I've done a lot of bad things. A lot of... But... it makes me want to do good.

And I nearly remembered the girls on the mattress. And I

hang on to the *tasbih*.

I thought I heard her say, *You are good man.*

I thought I heard someone.

How loud am I talking? *You are good man.*

—I'm not proud of it. The truth is, I was only there because... I was going along with it, you know?

Is she there? I don't know what I'm saying.

—Those girls, they just didn't care. I remember some of them—we were like animals! And next thing I hear, this girl, she went and... I calm down after that, you know... You know?

I'm not breathing. I can hear my heart. I can hear bare wailing on the wind, or rhythmic howling.

Is she there?

And I have to start breathing. And tears will come if I breathe too hard.

Watching the tiny twinkling lights.

15

I heard her call my name—

—and I'm woken with a flash of myself with a scrubby beard and white topi, reading Quran in a bare brick classroom with other *kameezed*-up mans. Where that come from? Perhaps it's a sign—I'm going *siratul mustaqeem*, be a proper Muslim, coz I can't take being near her like this.

I heard her call my name, and *Haji* has turned the lanterns low.

We look out the window frame—the distant headlights disappearing in and out of the range, coming closer.

And now it's close. But we can't see it, snarling up a mountain track—maybe a way leading to the shack.

And Haji tells her to leg it. And I follow her stumbling out of the doorway with her lantern, me with my iron bar, and I wave her on down the slope. Then I creep round the walls to watch the headlights jerk across the darkness and the slopes.

It stops some distance and the lights blink twice and go out.

We wait until a torchlight flickers on and off.

Some next man coming up a track. Maybe the same track our little goatherd trod. No point in warning him now.

And then my Dada is standing next to me. He moves forward and I go to stop him but he slowly releases my hand and climbs down.

The stranger stops and shines a torch on my man. They're talking in that language. So I go to front him and next man shines the torch in my face. He's muttering something and I can tell he's middle-aged and solid. And then he says:

—You are Khan sahib son?

—Yes. You're my uncle.

—Ha.

And I realise he may know my dad but he's not blood.

—Ha. And he?

—He's with me. He helped me.

—You have trouble?

—Yes.

There's this tense silence.

—No stay here.

Is it a question?

—No.

I must be screwing my eyes up bad because he shines it away.

—Trouble?

—Yes.

—*Dobra*. You say me what you say. I say if help.

And he points the torch at the shelter and glances at my man. I can guess what they're talking about—my man can parlez vous for me, but geezer saying he doesn't know him. He wants to talk to his '*bhateja*'.

And we go up to the shelter and I find the lantern and turn it up. And I realize I've got the iron bar and lay it on the window.

The bloke is bare gasping and searches for something in his jacket. I still haven't seen him properly, except he's got a serious growl.

And he gives me the watch back. I just stand there. So the little sheep shagger made it.

—Your Abu him call me Rahmat bey.

—I need to get out, I say.

He grunts.

—I need to get out.

—Problem. You have...?

And he rubs his fingers.

—Can you get this out?

And I give him the letter shining in darkness.

—Can you get this to the Embassy?

He grunts something like, *What is?*

—Embassy. British Embassy.

He's bare gasping over it, burning it with the torch.

—What is?

—Don't worry about it. I'm letting the British know I'm here.

—This Embassy?

—Yeah, the government.

If he says *What is* one more time...

And he shoves it in my chest practically. I'm gonna have to read it to the backward git. And in his torchlight I see:

Dear Card Services

Re: A/C 5455 7880 5167 6939 C

As you are aware my account has been in arrears and I have not made any payments for 5 months.

I'm not in a position to pay off the outstanding balance and have further debts with my Halifax current account also considerably overdrawn.

I've been advised by Citizens Advice Bureau that I can make a request to freeze the interest and arrange to pay monthly instalments.

My hands start shaking and I keep turning it over for the Embassy letter to magically appear.

—What is this!

And he says, *What is dis, ha?*

—What da fuck is this! Where's my letter! What da fff-aaarrggh!

And I run around the grimy shelter screaming and I can hear my man outside calling *Naseeb, Naseeb.*

Is that my signature? It's not my writing. I don't know what my writing is. Is it Amal? Why would she do that? How would she know about Halifax?

This geezer's trying a get me to shut up. But nothing is real.

My spar outside is calling *Naseeb, Naseeb.* And this bloke's saying *Nacip, Nacip.* He thinks I'm doolallay.

—I help. For your *Abu.* You him blood. Hah?

And he shakes me by the shoulder. And I'm emotional, like a boy. And he claps me a few more times. Embarrassed for me. Maybe he is blood.

—I need to get out. I need to get out.

And Rahmat *chaccha* grunts.

—I can take. Take to people. They take...

And he makes a gesture of going under or over.

—Can you take us to the border?

—We take. We take.

He doesn't sound convincing.

—Isn't there a phone? Can I call the Embassy?

—No phone.

—How can that be?

And my spar says something from the window and Rahmat isn't having it.

—Forget phone. You say before what happen.

—I don't know. I don't know what I'm supposed to have done.

—Must be something you do it.

—I did nothing!

He grunts.

—Did they say your fader?

—Say your father? My father's dead.

—Yes dead. Him dead. They say your fader?

And my Haji tries explaining.

—Ask about my dad? They didn't say anything.

—Because your dad. That why they...

—My dad? What about him?

—After kill him... of course them know you. Them know son him coming. Of course know when you coming. Of course know you.

I'm trying to stall. Trying to work out what's real. What

have I been dreaming?

—They killed him?

—Of course kill him.

—I thought he had cancer.

—They take him. Never again see. *Kalas*. That why you all this time England.

This *chaccha* is spooking himself at the window, listening out to shrieking things. My head is leaking. This bloke isn't real, my letter wasn't real, this place is not real. Who are all these people? The only thing real are those jackal-headed ghouls.

The old man is trying to talk to this Rahmat chaccha, but he's spooking himself at the window.

—You said if they asked about my dad...

—Ha?

—You said if they asked about my dad. How did you know I was picked up?

—I know... You listen someone? I want you no blame me for you fader.

—Why should I blame you?

—Just you no blame me—if I no do dis, do dat. Very problem. For every body. So you don't say me blame.

He's still staring into the black mountains.

—What you looking for?

—Nothing. I looking—just car. That side.

But a rat is eating my brain.

—I don't understand how there's no phone.

He taps his ears:

—No. Everything they know.

And then we all get shook by something rooting outside. And Rahmat switches off the torch.

—It's just a dog, I whisper. But I'm picking up the iron bar.

Something scurries fast on the slope, and this Rahmat geezer is screwing softly. I can smell his sweat. And I look out—

—It's just a dog.

And in the lantern dark I see the glint of his shooter, the glint of a gat in his hand.

—Dog?

—It's a dog.

I can see him ease the gun away, and switch on the torch. And he guesses I saw it:

—If need...

There's a rat gnawing. It gnaws that I know about Rahmat. From someone who knew Abba. Or from Abba. Or I saw him with Abba.

—I remember now. You were policeman. Or army.

He's pretending to look out the window.

—Not dis.

—You were though.

—No.

He's pretending to look out the window.

—You were border police weren't you?

—I help your Abu. But he make mess. Big problem. Problem me. Problem everyone! You don't thinking any bad. I help your fader!

I can't remember enough to say anything.

And then he says:

—I take you. I take people—they take. They help. But coming now. Okay?

I can't remember enough to say anything. So I follow him out, my Rahmat chaccha, coz I ain't got a plan.

And then he talks to my *dada*. And we're following in his steps across the slopes, his torch guttering the way. To his white clapping Lada pitched on the slope.

Even in the dark you can see it's loaded with crap. And then he's talking with Dad's Army again.

He opens the back door for my man and in the flashes of torchlight we see carpets and baskets. My chaccha bloke turns to me and makes signs of something being drawn over his head.

My man explains, *Hide*.

And Rahmat says, Yes.

And the stuff gets pulled out and my spar has to lie down and get covered up.

So where am I? The front seat looks like it's got a flipping washing machine. He takes me to the back, opens the boot:

—You must...

So he's left a washing machine in the front seat but he's cleared out the boot.

—You want me there? There!

But he just grunts to get on with it:

—Hide.

I'm looking at it.

—You must!

I must. What else am I gonna do? He's wondering why I'm getting in like an old man. It's like I'm in the box again. I'm in the box again. And just as he's ready to slam the blackness on me I shoot up my hand.

—Just a sec.

I'm feeling in my pocket.

—I haven't got my watch. I think I left my watch back there.

—Forget this.

—It's my dad's. I have to find it.

And I'm a lot quicker getting out.

—It must be in there. Let me just borrow the torch, *chaccha.*

But he holds on to it. And he comes and feels my pockets though I'm saying, *It's not there, it's not there, I left it on the window.*

—I go with.

—I'm just gonna run up and back.

—I go with.

Now I've got him on my back wheezing up the climb. My *chaccha* and his shooter.

And we hear scurrying on the slope. Then this steady growl. He throws the torch around and I know he's got the shooter.

All the way up we got this snarling getting us shook.

I slow up at the doorway, but I got no choice. I have to go in, act it out, go up to the window, look around, find my iron bar, scrape around the debris, stand there like a prick.

And then he says:

—Maybe look in pocket.

And I don't even bother pretending.

He's got his blammer.

We stand there.

—You helping me like you helped my dad?

—You fader bad man.

—So what have I done!

—You done.

So here we are. Him with his blammer. Me with my bar. And then there's the sickest growl outside. And my pig friend doesn't know where to flash the light.

—You say you dog go.

—It ain't mine.

—You say you dog go, or I shoot.

And just for an instant the torch catches a grey shape out of the door, and the flash of two yellow disks burning back—

the torch gutters and I go to move and the devil dog snarls harder and the pig shines it in my face—

that torch it gutters and the dog going mental, the torch it gutters and he shakes it and it goes out—

we hear Cujo come flying through the black, and next man's blammer lights up and shatters the walls with the devil dog surging from the ground—

the blammer lights up and fires and I mash the bar down on his arm—and me and the pig go bouncing off the wall as I lamp anything around til I'm busting up a groaning sack on the floor.

Someone kicked the torch back to life. And I see him curled under the wall, and no sign of the devil dog.

I go to pick up the torch and it's out again.

Just breathing in the dark.

—You break my arm!

—Tell me what you did, then! *Kutta sala!*

He's screwing at me in his own tongue.

—Tell me what you did, then!

He's saying *something-something-father-bastard.*

—You help my bastard dad then? Hey? Like this!

It's easier to hit him when I can't see, just hear the *banchod* cry.

He's cussing me down, then laughing.

Blah blah, he starts going, *blah blah dead man. Dead man!*

I start on the *banchod*, I want to make him eat his balls, he's like, *Yah, kill me! Come! Kill me! But you finish! You finish!*

And then in the yollering I can see him, like there's a glow coming in.

There she is in the doorway.

My pig *chaccha* groaning and cussing me out.

Amal with her hurricane lamp.

It's took my heart. I wanna say, *This isn't me. This isn't me.*

I drop the tool. And I pick up the torch, and a bottle of water.

That next man says, *Dead man.*

I've gone to the door and she looks straight past me at the battered *chattu*. And I've got to slink out like a criminal.

I say, *I'm sorry.*

And I'm gone.

I don't even know where I'm going. I'm leaving her. The stars are all trembling. And there's faraway rhythmic howling. I shout it to them all:

—I'm sorry!

And then there's the sound of someone climbing the slope. And I haven't got a tool, and my heart's been took. I don't run, I just stand there all moist, my torch flickering in the dark. And I can see someone coming.

Till the Old Man is on me and we stare at each other.

—What did you do, my friend?

And I says, *You talk too much.*

And without a word we are climbing up the ridge.

And me thinking, *This is how she remembers me. This is who I am.*

There's the voices on the wind. The squeal of wind and merged voices whipping along the ridge.

Listen! Those braying shouts, that must come from the shelter. We freeze, listen for her voice, but I only hear the roaring of the fat *suwar*. It rises and falls in agony, he's getting battered. Who by?

My feet want to turn back, but my man is climbing the ridge.

I'm listening for her voice, but only hear the fat *suwar*, and I follow my man. The roaring follows. And my body is strong.

Up on the top the wind kicks across. Pale desert below. Here is the track.

And we wrap the shawls close. This night cold has got into me, and my chest is burning.

And as we pick our way down, the screams have vanished, and below us rhythmic chanting.

Look. I never noticed those lights down there.

We stumble down with the guttering torch, the descent swallowed in darkness—

But I'm in the taxi place with da chronic mattress, and whole bunch a fam with the little skets... I wanna shout: *That's not me, man. That's not me. I can be good. I can be good...*

But I've slipped ends, a stairwell covered in gob and roaches, and some crew with a devil dog and lighty hench... who are they? The crew snickering like chimps, and I'm trying to...

trying to what?

What have I done? Have I done anything real? I don't remember anything that isn't shit. My head it's a mudhole where twisted creatures lie. Smiling and fronting to crutters fugly monkeys. Waiting for retribution. A Night of Power. And scenes a cowering bloodshed.

But that ain't me. Help me Allah. Help me remember You. Is it too late? It can't be too late.

Help me find Him, Amal. What's the rules? I want to save myself.

Oh shit. I'm too late.

We stumble down with the guttering torch. And I say to my man:

—Boss, I don't like myself.

And after time the chanting stops. It's just the sound of scraping blindly down the track.

Sometimes the track is just a goat run, that disappears, and then it's back. And below us a few lights scattered along an unseen road. My man doesn't slow or miss a step.

And then faraway voices are merged, and a high voice crying or declaiming, somewhere from a light below.

We are scrambling down to it, this clapping torch that's ready to die, and then it catches the gleam of two yellow disks; I thought it was lights from a house. Two yellow disks, just for a second, staring twenty feel below. It doesn't snarl, but we stop.

We wait.

Faraway the high voice is keening some story, a wavering anguished voice. And there are waves of howling responses.

I shake the torch and find the yellow disks. Staring back.

It's you, innit? It's you, Milo. You're probably standing there covered in shit with one leg chewed off. You come to make sure I don't leave.

I can't move.

My man he starts praying some protection. And he says softly to this thing:

—You want to know who we are? We are passing. We don't want to disturb you. Is it okay?

I can't move.

Then Haji runs straight down and vanishes into darkness. I'm thinking he's falling into darkness. And I hurry after, the torch flickering off, the darkness hiding ghosts and ripping fangs.

We stumble down on heels till the torch kicks in, and we've landed on our arse and slither down, and if we haven't broken a leg we can pick up the track again, and keep moving.

We keep moving, and there's no sign of the creature.

The keening and the chorus of voices rising.

The track is wider, dropping this way and that. There's a

light below, though I can't see the road.

And we're descending into waves of howling. Dropping onto a pale dome streaming orange light.

I can't keep up with the Haji.

I can see the outline of a small mosque or something. And a voice wailing a tale. And waves of weeping. They wouldn't hear us if we come down on an avalanche.

Dropping onto a clapping mosque, or a shrine. Or an old grain store. With people wailing. Where they all come from?

My man has sprung down the last bit of the slope and ghosted to the arching doorway. I can see through the doorway with the lanterns hanging on wires, bare heads with their boys all sitting on the floor, and next man keening this story; and a decorative screen, the kind Amal sat behind, and maybe the women are sitting there, and the menfolk and youngers all wailing on cue.

And there's a young kid, and when a wave of howling sweeps over the audience this kid looks like he doesn't understand a word, but next man with the story is crying, bare heads are crying, and he's sobbing to burst, looking round for help.

Nobody notices us.

This is a house of anguish, this is a house of ecstatic sorrows, and I'm a boy looking round at these keeners, and there's something in the lift and pain of the voice, that I see Muslims on a plain and swirling standards and spears, and forces in ambush and the fallen defenders and the martyred leaders.

Or maybe they're crying for themselves or something.

I nudge the Haji but he doesn't want to go, like he knows them.

Nobody notices as we scrape. And cross the mountain road.

And it's a long time down before they fade.

There's a flare on the horizon that spreads up like smoke, and I can almost see the broken skin of the desert. And it's freezing.

The torch is almost dead.

Now a *dhikr* chant is floating somewhere.

Thank God this side is easier. I can see the slope like a gloomy carpet of sheepskins. I'm staring so hard it keeps shifting and blacking out. And my head is floating somewhere.

The edge of the desert is nearly there.

And it's just the sound of our heels scraping down. Thank God this side is easier.

And then something cracks above us, and ricochets off the mountain and over our heads. And then another explosion that flashes on the mountain. Where we came from.

We stand on the slope. But hear no screams. No wailing. No keening. We hear a soft rain of clods falling in the darkness.

We look at darkness.

Allahu Akbar, says my man.

And then we're scraping down the slope. Followed by nightmares of the creatures that did it.

Maderchod. Maderchod.

The edge of the desert is always nearly there.

And there's something on the bottom. Like surf, like scum.

It licks around and blurs the murk of the desert.

And then we are down on the desert.

A wrinkled paleness that disappears into murk. Into mist.

And I see him praying some *du'a* or *salah*. And I want to tell him, *I'm gonna die here with you, Haji.*

But I see him kiss the ground and he's praying some *du'a* or *salah*.

And I haul that *bhenchod* with me.

16

Rabba naaa akhrijnaa min haazihil qaryatiz-zaalimi ahluhaa; waj 'al lanaa milla dunka waliy-yanwwaj 'al lanaa milla dunka nasiiraa...

We hurry, hurry. My old limbs and his wounded leg keep pace with each other.

—What are we doing, boss?

We hurry to our fate. Quickly, is there no good deed to run ahead! What have I done? Did I never serve You, Allah? Something ill moves in me. Ah, then let me forget. I am lost. I am lost.

—You're what?

And I realise I spoke the last aloud.

All I can remember is an ugly cat attacked by dogs. It hid in bushes and limped out to everyone in passing. It mewled like a dried-up tea chest and would soon die without drinking. It wanted to follow me as I carried on. And I returned with milk and a pigeon leg. That day I was with Allah. My mother would not allow me to bring home its fleas, but I returned for three days to feed it until a party of men camped for the night, and I never saw it again.

I could have saved my cat. Did I do enough to be saved by my cat?

It should be day. But there is a mist like hoarfrost in my eyes. It shrouds the distance.

Creatures call from nowhere.

The boy is looking, looking. And he says, *Do you see that?* It's gone.

And then he says, *There.*

For a long time I see nothing but the murk. And then I see the shape, a distant bundle on the ground, like a dead animal.

And he moves further away, closer to the shape.

—Naseeb, I say. For this mist is strange. A mist in a desert. A fog.

—Naseeb.

—Quiet.

And suddenly the bundle gets up, and starts running.

We are frozen. It is running with flowing robe or coat. A shade is running back to the mountain.

—Naseeb!

But he is trying to run, chasing the shade. They run towards the veiled mountain, on and on, and the fog will envelop them. Till he runs without hobbling, runs and catches her—I hear her cry, I hear them tumble down exhausted.

Hurry, hurry. There—the man breathless, and she a spare woman, pulling her burka around her and wailing.

He's telling her, Don't scream. He's not going to hurt her, does she understand.

And she is wailing in her own tongue:

—*I beg you sir, have mercy! I did nothing! I did nothing! Ya Ghafurul Rahim! May Allah show mercy.*

The boy stands up and feels his sore joints. And he makes her stand up, and blocks her from running to the mountains.

—Naseeb *jan*, what are you doing?

She looks wildly at me and comes with raised hands. A spare, sharp-faced woman, not young.

—*Oh, sir, have mercy. Please let me go to my baby.*

She falls at my feet. And I tell her she is safe, and give her water from the boy's bottle. But she sits there crying.

—She says she has a baby. What do you want with this woman?

—She came from out there. How far? How far to border?

She sees him pointing back to the desert and is frightened. She is saying something—we cannot go that way. She points to the veiled mountains behind us—this way.

But the boy is gesturing back:

—You came from there? From there? Tell her. The other side?

—She says she has a baby, she wants to go back to her baby.

—Ask her! Ask her if she came from there.

I try to calm her and ask her. And she nods.

—She came alone?

—Alone? I ask. And she nods.

—Are there soldiers? Soldier!

She shakes her head.

And he is thinking.

—Is there water? Waterhole?

He points to his plastic bottle and into the desert.

—We have water, I say.

She nods unsurely.

—How far is water?

She looks to me and when I explain she answers vaguely.

—Ten miles, I say.

She sits there under her burka, knees drawn under her chin. Like a prisoner.

—Where's her baby?

And when I ask her she nods toward the mountain. Back

to where we came from. And he smiles bitterly.

—Ye-eah, right... She has to come with us.

—We have water, I say.

—Just to the water. Then she can come back.

—We have water.

—Did you notice anything back there? Those Klingons may be right on our heels. She can run straight to them. She has to come part of the way. Then at least we've got a headstart.

—She will not say anything. She is frightened. Let her go.

—You know, for someone who didn't give a shit about his own life, you're pretty free with mine. She's coming, chaccha! Get up! Get up, lady! You take us—just to water. Then you can go.

And when she thinks she understands she wails to me again.

—She says she is hiding from them. She cannot say anything. This is unnecessary.

—Unnecessary! Now you're talking, old man! Unnecessary is you pissing on every step I make. I don't remember asking you to tag along. What are you waiting for? You wanna go—go. But she's coming.

He stands there a boy acting like a man.

I say to the woman we heard an explosion, there may be bad people coming. But she has decided if she sits and cries we may leave her.

—Tell her to be quiet! I've had it!

He drags her after him but she digs her heels and screeches.

—Shut up! Shut up! Shut your goddamn neck!

And his hand goes down hard on her face.

—Naseeb, stop!

She wants to cry out but he has put force on her neck. And I cannot break his grip.

—You want to die here?

I say, *Please, bhai. You don't wish this.*

And he hisses to her, *Be quiet. Just to water.*

And I tell her, **Go—come back. It will be all right.*

He hauls that woman to her feet and they stand there shaking. Then says to me:

—And you, what are you waiting for? You're no use to me.

He drags the weeping woman after him. And I follow.

The sun burns through and dissolves the mist.

The mountains fickle pink.

They sweep around our sides and the desert basin is cracked in thousands of pieces with twists of straggly bushes and fraying soil.

And behind us a grey spindle of smoke on the mountain.

Where the dead and living are scattered.

And the boy says nothing for a long time.

She struggles to keep up.

He says:

—I've been remembering this kid, boss... a bunch a boys... some kid gets smashed in the face with an umbrella. And he's running... holding this blood in his hands. Like, what's he going to do with the blood? And thing is... I don't know if I'm the kid... or I'm the one who...

She struggles to keep up.

—You tired? It's okay. I'm sorry. You understand? I'm sorry. Tell her I'm sorry.

What can I say to him? What is to say his path was worse than mine? I had thought nine hundred thousand *rakats* had built a raft against ruin. I wore my beard a fist's length and left my ankles uncovered. I followed the sternest *fiqh*: guarded my body from a woman's brush and my nostrils from her scent; kept the times of *salat*; calculated *zakat* to a grain and the *farz* of permitted limits to a hair's breadth. With my brothers we confirmed the commentaries, sought out *bida* and *shirk*, and cursed the grave worshippers and chess players. Where are my brothers now? Can they speak for me and lead me into Gardens? Allah knows what is in our hearts. Let me forget. Here is the secret: O Allah, You forgot to make me a man.

She says she cannot walk. I know he will not pause.

Ya Qawiyy, Ya Qawiyy, Ya Qawiyy, Ya Qawiyy.

Listen!

A cry, of a wailing reedpipe, or an evil spirit that brays in the distance!

We turn to the mountain and see only a spindle of grey smoke.

Somewhere bleating spirits that bray with dead eyes and blackened skin—*Allah Hafiz!*

—Do you hear it, says the boy.

But she doesn't even hear us.

She is limping, signs to him she cannot walk.

—Here, lean on me. It's okay. Come, you can do it.

Soon it will be too warm for jackets.

Now I walk ahead of them. She leans completely on Naseeb who grimaces.

What is that sound? A low distant thump of mining. Or engines crushing. We hear it, but don't speak.

—What's your baby? Boy? Girl? Ask her, Haji. How old is he? Is he strong? He wants *dudh*? Don't worry, Amma. He's going to see you no time. Tell her, Haji.

She wants water. And he gives her the bottle.

A distant sound of engines crushing. It sounds louder but as far away.

And a braying reed seems to shriek from one side of the horizon to the other. Does she hear it? For she is saying, No, no, no.

She falls to the ground despairing. Ah, her leg is too painful. She tells me:

—*I can't walk on, I can't walk back. Yallah help me. What will become of us?*

—We cannot take her, bhai. Let her go, she is a burden.

—I'm not leaving you here. Come on.

What is he doing? He is already gone mad. He makes her stand then puts her on his back!

—You will not survive like this, bhai. You need to rest. She needs to rest.

—She's getting a rest.

I let him stagger away, with her wailing like a new bride plucked up by the groom's side. He must realise his madness. But he staggers on and slowly I follow.

Finally I hear him groan and fall with the woman on top of him.

And what shall make him understand? When a woman picks up a plastic bottle and smashes it in his face?

The woman picks up the bottle and smashes it in his face.

He cries out—and I watch as she picks up her skirts and sprints across the cracked desert to the mountain.

I hurry to Naseeb, and when he can see again after the blow to his broken nose we watch her run for an age. She looks back over her shoulder once and starts running again.

I say, *You gave her a good rest.*

Say, the plastic bottle is split at the bottom, though I can hold it upside down.

—*Kutti sala.* That's our water.

He wants to go after her but she will be a speck. And we cannot go back. We must go on before the sun is high.

We must walk or die.

What is that pounding? What is that in the pounding?

Keep the sun to the left. There are rifts and scrubby rises in the distance. And a horizon of blue hills or mountains or clouds.

Walk.

What is that mewling?

It is too hot for jackets. The boy is asking how much water was lost.

But there is a sound coming from a sage bush tangle. And now it is I who veer away to approach it. And reach a small bundle of cotton.

—What is it, the boy calls.

And I stoop to look inside the cloth.

—What is it, he calls.

But I stay kneeling until he comes.

The baby cries weakly.

And what can make us understand a baby wrapped in cotton? Its eyes shut and its hand closing and grasping.

—She left her baby. She left her baby to die. That *chotta*—

He spins to see if the woman is visible.

—Damn you! Damn you to Hell!

Is he laughing or crying?

I say, *The child will die.*

—You wanna go back for her!

And then he blasphemes Allah, curses me for bringing him here, curses us all, and falls to the ground crying.

—Why? Why?

The baby cries weakly. With one hand curled over his eyes.

And suddenly I am taken to a street outside a cornershop. And in the middle of the pavement with people stepping by was a spotless white cat, almost a kitten, it was stretched out on its front with both paws covering its eyes as if to cut out the pain and humiliation as it lay dying. I stopped to see if anyone laid claims on it, why it was stretched out like this. And I walked on. Now I know what you are.

And I have picked up the baby.

Can we go back? Go forward? Who will take this baby? I try to picture it. But this baby was given for a reason.

The man is shaking his head, looking at endless desert.

—It's finished.

—I must find my cat. My cat is there.

—You what?

And my feet already going forward. My feet racing across the riven ground.

He calls:

—Chaccha! That's my water! Chaccha! You're both gonna die!

—I must find my cat.

—Yes. You go and find your marbles. You doddering git.

How long have I carried?

My feet kick through clods. And sage bush and dust hills. Naseeb is calling somewhere behind me, he cannot keep up.

I feel its skin and bones stretch and jerk. It cries and is

silent.

How long have I carried him?

I don't know if I'm awake and my eyes are closed. And I am in a darkened coach travelling through night, across the black fields and scrub; crossbars of light passing through the coach hull, over the silhouetted heads, running off handrails like silverfish. Lights passing backwards and forwards. Everyone motionless in the constant rumble of gears.

It seemed I saw the unseen landscape sheering along the walls of my head—the red lights of other buses the colour of pomegranate lit from within—

and then I was fallen in the dust! and my mouth bloodied, and my hands still holding the baby.

And after a time Naseeb reaches me and lifts the baby who is protected by his angels.

—*Hamdulillah*, he says.

I sit up in the dust, my mouth bloodied and numb. The sun has crossed to my left. I have turned back to the mountains.

And he examines the bottle which is nearly drained in the fall.

—You alright, chaccha? We should rest.

He uncovers the pursed face—a few droplets of water from

his finger fall on baby's mouth. He dabs more drops to the mouth, and the face becomes alive, and the baby sucks on his finger. And I see sorrow on the man's face, it wells up and overflows his eyes.

—*Haramzaada.*

He wants to wash my wound. But we have no water. We must go. He makes a turban for me out of my jacket. And the same for himself.

—Let's find the waterhole, chaccha.

To the water, I vow. And we turn back south.

The boy carries the baby and hurries across the scrub. I can hardly keep up.

Does he talk to the baby?

—Is it too late? Maybe it's too late. I can do it like it's not too late. I mean what are you gonna do? Thank you, little bro. I know this isn't real. But what I'm doing is real.

Walk and die.

If the sky could bring a cloak of clouds. A wave rushing with outstretched arms.

If I could see You Allah...

There are black spots as I close my eyes longer and longer.

And closing my eyes I lose the sense of an outside world. It appears only in flashes.

Surely He guides us to evil or to gardens.

Let us give up completely to be in Your gardens of sweet springs. Let us be Your instruments, Allah, for this child.

We will tread circles.

Once this was a lake bed or sea, where we are left floundering—creatures of muddy shallows misshapenly grasping with eel mouth.
Walk and die.
Because we can do no other.

How long does he carry?

I who dreamed in prison of seeing Your sky, Your mountains, Your circling eagles—I must close my eyes.
I have forgotten what I thought.

I don't remember when the desert became rock.

I forget there is someone else. I think that I am carrying the child.

I forget what I thought.

I forget there is someone else. He is howling. Or crying, Naseeb is crying like a wounded calf. Where is he?

He has fallen. He has fallen on his side on the edge of a drop. Where the crust of the desert floor has broken like old bread.

Yallah! He has dropped the baby over the edge!

I stagger up, but the baby is safe in the crook of his arm. And the boy is lowing like an animal.

What is he looking at? The drop is but ten feet, and the ground arcs down to a sheltered bottom, where another small hole gleams darkly.

I have been sightless for so long it hardly feels real.

I dare not believe.

Allahu Akbar. Have You brought us to relief, my Lord?

I try to lift up the boy and we hobble down to the tiny waterhole. And in the shade of sedimentary rock we unwrap the baby to see if he is living.

And then we wash our hands and faces and drink. *Allahu Akbar.*

And I wet the baby's bright red face, and his matted black hair. Who cries completely silent. And I feed him from my little finger. And he clamps his mouth on my finger and a shock went through my arm and into my innards; and I felt like I was looking at an old man from a far distance; and no longer knew what was living and what was dead.

Naseeb drips water into the baby's mouth.

—Uncle, is he bigger? You think he's bigger? He looks bigger.

The baby staring at the boy, and his mouth rounding in an 'O', and his tongue slowly pointing round. Or rather the baby looks over the boy's shoulder, twisting to frown over his other shoulder. His black eyes seeking out shadows around our shapes.

—He's trying to tell me something. Come on, bro, drink more. You still need milk, don't you? We'll find for you.

He takes off the baby's sheet. And a flannel nappy with a green smear.

—You want washing, little *bhaiya*? Don't give me a nasty surprise, okay?

And I make *wudhu*. And he washes the baby's body on his lap while I beat the nappy on the flat rock. And he stops washing the baby and looks at his back.

—Damn. We really are brothers. Hey, Baba, my man here has a birthmark just like mine.

He takes off his shirt and tries to look at his shoulder.

—What do you think?

And I am afraid. The birthmarks are the same.

—What do you think? he says, as he washes himself.

—You are one.

—What do you mean?

—You are one.

He tries to see his reflection in the pool.

—What do you mean?

And he is fearful. He looks at me for explanation, for reassurance. While I make *wudhu*. Did I just made *wudhu*?

—It's not real. This place has fried my brains. I'm gonna wake up and find I've been carrying a coconut all this time.

I wash my arms, wipe my hair, my neck. And I too am fearful. I have spent so long imprisoned I have become a stranger to my body and myself.

We rest in turns, carrying the baby. If we had time we could lie here till the sun was low. Rested and hidden by night.

But he cries.

—I know, little *bhai*, but we can't go now. See that sun? See that? Gonna hurt you. Gonna fry you like toast. Can you hang on a bit? Just a bit. I promise you, bhai. You'll have gallons of *dudhu*. How could anyone do that to him? That *kutti salla*, I hope they blow her *pudhee* to pieces.

He cries so hard we wonder how he has strength.

—All right, little feller. I'll get you a new mommy. A beautiful, kind mommy. And we'll all live together. Yeah, we'll all live together.

Till he quietens and our bodies deflate on the broad, smooth rock. My body will not get up.

The man is resting on the broad flowing rock. Resting because the child is still on his chest.

I am resting.

17

He dreamed he was in the mountain shelter where he lay stricken in the darkness. And the broken roof showed no stars. And a light came to the doorway.

Help me, he called.

And it was Amal, but so tall, so tall her feet cannot be treading the floor beneath the long black lengha. Cold light pours from her. And she holds something in her hand that scrapes the floor.

Then he heard a man's voice. And it came from Amal.

*What did you do?

And he was gripped with horror.

*What did you do with these hands?

And he could hear himself moaning in sleep.

And she raised the iron bar above her head—and he didn't know what creature it was that swung it down—

And I'm suddenly awake. Because the child is still. And something like an eagle squealing in the sun.

I creep closer.

The baby's mouth drawn open and his lips peeling, his

eyes rolled up under lids, and his breath whistling in short rasps. One hand is tangled in the hairs of Naseeb's chest. I feel for his other hand and he grips my thumb for a moment then loosens.

I shake the man gently but he will not wake. Again and again. And then he jerks up blinking:

—What?

—We must go.

He sits breathing heavily, his dream receding.

—Now? It's not even... it's not even...

And I take off my yellowing shirt and tear the tail and tie the arms to make a sling, and put it round my neck for the baby.

—You serious? You been sitting in jail for the last century, and now you gotta go? We can't make it, Haji. Not in this.

—We must make it.

I reach for the baby, and Naseeb gets up quickly.

—Dada wait. Wait a minute.

The baby's hand still tangled in the man's chest, I hold his other hand, and he grips my fingers.

—I'm trying to do the best for him.

—And I too.

The baby's hand tangled in his chest, his fingers hold my hand.

—Naseeb. We cannot wait, then spend the remaining

daylight wandering. To end in darkness. We cannot wait. He cannot wait.

And I go to our jackets and soak them in the water, and I fill the broken bottle. And I tie my jacket round my head. And I offer him his jacket, and he is staring. He is staring at my shoulder. I know what he sees. And I grow afraid.

What seems unreal is staring at us.

What was real is a dream. A dream of a burning desert and parched outcasts. A child made of nothing. A faint band of mountains shimmering mauve.

So why should we make another step?

But the child stretches stiff jerking arms and tries to cry with shrivelled lips.

The man stares at me, at my shoulder.

—Haji. What is this place?

And I am afraid to look at him.

That youth he washes himself and the baby, and drips water in the baby's mouth. And he ties the jacket to his head and asks for the sling and puts the baby in. And he covers the baby with his shirt.

I say, We must find a road. The border will not be far.

But he has hobbled out into the desert. With faint blue mountains to draw us on.

May Allah reveal to me the spiritual rank of this youth. O bearer of mercy, grant me knowledge of your special knowledge!

And the heat falls on us like tarp.

And the baby silent.

There are black spots as I close my eyes longer and longer.

Our faces blister into cured meat.

La ilaha illallah... La ilaha illallah...

I have become colourless, tasteless, bodiless.

I am dreaming. Guttering lights are throwing shadows in the prison where an old man is dying on a litter, and a dead dog in the corner...

I am still dreaming. The doctors in filthy *kameezes* are making plaster of Paris in a blackened trough, and porters fitting a raggedy child with a leg from a shop mannequin...

I am walking... or dreaming...

Who is carrying the baby?

I am awake!

Has he fallen? The man is holding my sleeve pulling me down, with the baby tucked in his shirt. The man pulls me down, squinting to the blue mountains. I can hardly open my eyes. It looks like horizon shimmer. But he signals me to flatten.

And the horizon raises a white dust trail, and then a glint moving.

He hugs the baby close and we scramble to a dried alluvial gouge in the plain, its shallow banks crumbling and pitted with vanished roots.

We crouch there with the baby mewling, till we hear the drone of the jeep and its dust trail rises.

If it crosses the dried bed we are visible. But it sweeps alongside the trench, with something trailing the jeep, scouring the dust behind.

The man he stares. And the baby crying louder. But I have seen the tethered shape scouring the dust behind.

And we hear the jeep buffeting along the bank, and it roars dread in our ears, with the baby screaming, and we cower under the bank, as it snarls over our heads, before the dread falls away, and the baby crying.

And Naseeb puts his eyes over the bank, but I have seen those monstrous riders with the jackal-reptile masks.

When we step out of the trench the jeep is disappearing

back to the same blue band. Trailing a tethered shape like bait.

And we stand there, the man rocking the baby, knowing we must follow.

I unwrap the head of the baby.

—He looks older, Baba. Doesn't he look older?

The baby opens his shrivelled mouth. And a single hopeless mewl. And he twists his head searching for a dug.

—I can't take it, Baba. I can't take wanting to help. Baby, don't you know I'm powerless?

We walk fast.

There's a rhythmic rasping—is it the child or man?—urging us, to fly to hills and shallow lakes, to bring an end to suffering.

But the strength soon drains. And tongues lick blistered lips. And we walk blinded in dream.

Who is that rasping?

Every time I open my eyes I have stumbled far from them.

Some time we stop and he unwraps the baby's face. Two veins meeting in his forehead. And the mouth twisting like a mudfish.

And I take the sling and the baby, a baby made of nothing, and walk into the blaze.

An old man and a boy. Or a man.

My life is over, Lord, let this creature live before me. Let this man live before me.

I'm trying little son.

But soon enough I am stumbling and I don't know if I am walking or dreaming.

Boy, you are too heavy for me. Made of nothing, you are too

Someone   is breathing *Hay hay hay hay hay...*

Is it me?

Every time I open my eyes I have stumbled far

... the boy...

... he has stumbled far...

... a shape, a bundle on the ground, like a dead animal.

And he moves closer to the shape, a dead animal.

—Naseeb, I say.

But I know already. And I hold my baby to my chest.

And what will make you seek forgiveness? Inside a tattered burka the broken body of a mother. A spare, sharp-faced woman, not young. An animal in a shroud. And the shredded skirts have ridden up her legs, and the cords still bind her ankles.

I am standing in the jeep tracks where they dragged her like bait and cut her loose.

If there was one thing I could say to you... but I don't know what to say to you.

The man takes the baby and sling from me. We look at the baby's face. His chin fallen down and his eyes rolled under lids.

The man lashes his crooked body faster. And I can't keep up.

But I see a distant line running in the desert. I see a dark blot. And I think I see the shadow of something... of wires or posts or something.

I can't keep up.

My life is over, Lord, let this creature live before me. Let this man live before me.

Why am I walking?

An old man.

Or a man... a man.

And Allah.

Do you remember Allah?

Do you remember a cat?

... a dark school room... a tin-roofed... My brothers! What are we doing? What are we doing?

Can I recite my verses? Can I find an *ayah* to help? My mouth is moving. My feet are moving.

When did the salt desert turn to sand? It shovels over my sandals.

And in my sleep I think the ground is shaking to hammer blows.

Is it our feet? Is there a mine here? A constant muffled concussion underground.

And my closed eye sees the desert split open and strutting spider legs the size of a crane breaking out, and the bullet body blacks out the sun, and its legs straddle over us like pylons.

The ground shaking to hammer blows.

And then my sandals slap on hard road, and I look for Naseeb, but he is not ahead, and I look along the dust-coloured road to a limping figure.

Can you see a man hurry to a far-off clutch of huts, and beetle-like crowds, and the hum of trucks and buses?

The dust-coloured road disappearing through a tiny watchtower into the clutch of huts—see the glint of binoculars!

And the mountains wavering.

I try to call him... there the faint gauze of a fence running from the checkpoint and disappearing into the desert.

I try to call but my throat is powerless.

I try to call him back—we must turn away from the checkpoint, leave this road, find a crossing further along the fence.

Can you see a man hurrying to his doom?

I start to run.

Something is coming from the checkpoint—a bus that turns from the man and heads to wavering mountains. See the glint of windows! And the man clutching his charge trying to wave it down.

I start to run.

Can you see a man clutching his charge, willing to sacrifice himself at the checkpoint?

In his arms the Black Stone.

Allahu Akbar Allahu Akbar, La ilaha illallahu Allahu Akbar

Allah reveals to me the man! O bearer of Mercy! While we the dead circumambulate the living!

My trembling limbs quicken of themselves, till they reach the man—and I kiss the bundle wrapped to his body.

—Only now have I made my Haj.

Naseeb half wakes, puts his arm around the baby, and tries to leave me behind. And I fight to take his hand, and kiss his hand, and put it to my forehead.

—Only with you could I be found.

The youth croaks, *Gerroff me, you mo.*

Hay hay hay hay hay hay hay hay

Are they watching us—two outcasts straggling in from nowhere?

The man shuffling trying to shout:

—*Maashallah, maashallah.* Help me. Please. The baby needs help. Baby needs hospital.

By the two soldiers who stroll out from the compound.

—I had... I had accident. Accident. Please I need to get the baby to hospital.

I summon the last of my strength to reach him—

Hay hay hay hay

We get as close as they will allow, their rifles casually

trained, the soldiers talking first in one tongue then in English:

—Where from? Papers. Papers. Where from?

—Back there... Please, baby has to go to hospital straight away. Does anyone speak English?

This soldier with lush moustache steps forward with rifle in one arm to check the bundle.

—Baby will die.

The soldier lifts part of the shirt—he springs back yelling!

They train their rifles on Naseeb yelling and backing away. The others are alerted and I can hear the clack of their rifles.

—No! no! A baby! Baby needs milk! There's nothing wrong. Baby needs milk.

They shout, *Hands up! Hands up!* They shout at me to keep away from him—*On the ground! On the ground!*

The checkpoint guards start running forwards. They are barking from the tower.

—*No, brothers, I wave back. No, brothers. Friend. Help.*

—No, no! please! What are you—? I'm not—please, the baby needs...

He unveils the baby, and we look down on a bundle of red and white wires and cigar-shaped pipes.

—No... no...

We look down on the bomb wrapped in my shirt.

And the man looks up and says hopelessly, *I've got a baby.*
I've got a baby.

More soldiers bellowing from the fences. And beyond
them I see a man slipping from the crowds in his kurta and
leather jacket, clutching his backpack. And even from here I see
his disbelieving eyes—

desert phantoms, sun blistered, beaten and bruised—he
sees himself!

This Naseeb by my side that looks down at a bundle of
pipes and wires, and looks up:

—What do you want, Allah! What do you want! I've got
nothing! I've got nothing!

I have seen you all:

the soldiers holding back the queues, abandoning the
molested mother, the fat captain waving an arm here and an arm
there... I can even hear the old radio...

I can see you, Naseeb—in your clean kurta and rucksack,
backing away from the boyish guards, from the buses and trucks—

Do you see me?

Say, *Run, run from this place. Throw your bag! Throw it!*

And this Naseeb by my side—who cries for his lost baby,
cries to the soldiers, *What do you want from me, Allah! I got nothing!*

They are training rifles, screaming orders, but daren't

shoot—for fear of the nails or bearings...

Baba! he cries, like a broken-mouthed baby. Baba!

Here I am, Naseeb, here. Let me hold you like a baby. *Astaughfirullah*, let me save you.

They are screaming at us—*hands on head, on the ground, on the ground!*

Can you see me, Naseeb, through your tears? Let me hold you like Mercy. And we hold each other; and just for a moment, as we lower our heads, and a volley of gunfire cracks around us, I see the baby curled in his sling, with chin dropped deathly open, and the skin peeling from shrivelled lips, and his hand curled over his eyes...

And then a sun explodes to melt man and baby in a flash of love...

GLOSSARY

A

Astaughfirullah – *Arab*. lit. 'Forgive me Allah'

B

Baggamans – n. lot of people

Baraka – *Arab. pl. barakat* n. blessing, spiritual energy

Bare – adj. many, a lot of

Batty – adj. *derog*. gay

Bait – adj. obvious

Beta – *Urdu* n. man, son

Bhabi – *Urdu* n. older brother's wife

Bhai, Bhaisap – *Urdu* n. brother

Blam, blammer – n. handgun,

Borer – n. knife

Bless – adj. good, okay

Bowl – v. to swagger down street

Boy (off) – v. to insult, curse down,

Braaap – *excl*. expressing excitement, assent, mimicking gunfire

Bredders – n. brothers, mates

Breeze – n. hot air, rubbish, *chatting breeze*

Breeze – v. to run, go fast

Bun – v. to smoke

Butters – adj. ugly

C

Chacha – *Urdu* n. paternal uncle

Chat – v. to lie

Chronic – adj. can mean good or bad smelling

Chups – v. action of sucking or kissing teeth, expressing irritation

Clapping – adj. out of date, worn out

Click – n. gang

Cotch – v. to chill, relax

Creps – n. trainers, running shoes

Crump – *excl.* adj. can mean good, bad, shocking

Crutters – adj. mashed up

D

Dada – *Urdu* n. paternal grandfather, an elder

Dadi–ma – *Urdu* n. paternal grandmother

Dash – v. to throw out

Deadout – adj. useless

Deff (it) – *Brum.* v. forget it, give it up

Dook – v. beat (up)

Draw – n. marijuana

Drum – n. drum and bass music, grime

Du'a – *Arab*. n. supplicatory prayer

Dunya – *Arab. Urdu* n. the temporal world

E

Edge up – *imp*. 'Come out my face'

Ends, endz – n. neighbourhood

F

Farz – *Arab*. adj. obligatory (prayers or practices)

Five–O – n. police (from *Hawaii Five-O*)

G

Garms – n. clothes

Giving air – v. to ignore someone

Gash – n. *derog*. girl, female

Grease – n. rubbish

Gyaldem – n. *sing. & pl*. female, girlfriends

H

Haji – *Arab. hon*. n. an elder who has made Haj pilgrimage

Hamdulillah – *Arab*. lit. 'Praise to Allah'

Heads – n. people

Hype – adj. over the top, too much, n. trouble

I

Iman – *Arab.* n. faith

Is-it – *excl.* expressing surprise

Island – *Brum.* n. a roundabout

J

Jack – v. to steal

Jam – v. to relax, *jam your hype*

Janaza – *Arab.* n. funeral rites

Jannah – *Arab.* n. Paradise

Jarring – adj. annoying

Jazaakallah – *Arab.* lit 'Thanks to Allah'

Juz – *Arab.* n. a division of the Quran

K

Keris – n. Indonesian short sword

Kufic, Shikaste, Thuluth – *Arab. Pers.* n. styles of calligraphy. A
     'hand' means a calligraphic style

Kurta – *Urdu Pers.* n. collarless shirt, tunic

L

Lamp – *Brum.* v. to hit, beat

Licky – adj. high, intoxicated

Lighty – n. light-skinned person

Long – adj. time-consuming, nuisance

M

Masha'allah – *Arab.* lit. 'as Allah willed it'

Mash – n. handgun

Mash – v. destroy

Mandem – n. male, males, male friends

Mans, manz – *pron.* I, me

Mishti – *Urdu* n. sweets

Moved to – v. to be deceived

Mouth – n. front youth of a gang

Murk, murkalize – v. to insult, destroy, kill

Musafir – *Arab. Persian. Urdu* n. traveller, exempt from fasting

N

Namaz – *Persian, Urdu* n. formal prayer

Next man – n. someone, random person

Nudge – n. bump fists

O

Older – n. someone older or senior in status who has your back

On road – adv. around

P

P's, Papers – n. money, notes

Penging – adj. strong smelling

Pickney – n. baby

Po–po – n. police

R

Raa, raah – *excl.* amazement, disapproval, etc

Rinsed – adj. worn out, old

Rooza, Rooja – *Arab. Urdu Farsi* n. fasting

S

Safe – adj. all right, no worries

Sahaba – *Arab.* n. pl. the Companions, those who followed the Prophet in his time

Salwar – *Urdu* n. baggy thin trousers, *salwar kameez*, two-piece with thin shirt

Samje – *Urdu* v. understand

Score – n. £20 bag of drugs

Scrape – *imp.* go away! v. to go away

Screw – v. argue, moan at

Screwface – n. person with angry or dirty looks

Shook – adj. scared, nervous

Shot – v. sell drugs *p.p.* sold drugs

Shotter – n. drug dealer

Skeen – adj. seen, understood

Silat – n. Indonesian-Muslim martial art

Slip (ends) – v. go into another gang's area

Subhanallah – *Arab.* lit. 'Glory to Allah'

Swingers – n. people fighting

Switch – v. go into a rage

T

Tap – v. have sex with

Tasbih – *Arab. Urdu* n. rosary beads used in zikr

Tool – n. weapon, *tooled up*

Tonk – adj. muscular, big

W

Wasteman – n. useless, goalless person

Wet – v. go fast, open up the throttle

Whip – n. car

Wudhu – *Arabic.* n. ritual ablution for prayer

Y

Yard – n. house, neighbourhood

Yonks – *Brum.* n. long time, ages

Younger – n. one younger or lower in status

Z

Zaat – *Arab.* n. essence

Zikr, Dhikr – *Arab.* lit. 'remembrance', chanting of Allah's
    attributes

Zoot – n. spliff